T0321371

Paradigms of the Large-Scale Universe

Paradigms of the Large-Scale Universe

V.G. Gurzadyan
Yerevan Physics Institute, Armenia

A.A. Kocharyan
Monash University, Victoria, Australia

Gordon and Breach Science Publishers
Switzerland • Australia • Belgium • France • Germany • Great Britain
India • Japan • Malaysia • Netherlands • Russia • Singapore • USA

Gordon and Breach Science Publishers S.A.
World Trade Center
Case postale 531
1000 Lausanne 30 Grey
Switzerland

British Library Cataloguing in Publication Data

Gurzadyan, V.G.

Paradigms of the Large-Scale Universe
I. Title   II. Kocharyan, A.A.
523.10151

ISBN: 2-88124-966-3

Cover: Geometry and the Universe by Ara Gurzadyan depicting geometry and the Universe as an infinite space.

To our parents

Contents

PREFACE

Recent decades have been a time of exciting observational discoveries concerning the large-scale structure of the Universe. Though even greater advances might be anticipated for the forthcoming decades, the present situation in the field already resembles that of the dynamics of galaxies in the 1940s which enabled Chandrasekhar to make an attempt *"to present the theory of stellar dynamics as a branch of classical dynamics - a discipline in the same general category as celestial mechanics"* in his classic book *Principles of Dynamics of Stellar Systems*.

Though considered to be governed by the same Newtonian gravitational interaction, the dynamics of clusters of galaxies differs drastically from stellar dynamics and therefore, for a proper treatment, requires a different mathematical approach.

On the other hand spectacular progress has been made in the theory of dynamical systems, providing powerful methods for the study of profound properties of many-dimensional nonlinear systems. Since any physical problem can be reduced to a model described by a certain nonlinear system, the outstanding importance of such achievements as the proof of the Kolmogorov-Arnold-Moser (KAM) theorem, the discovery by Kolmogorov of a new metric invariant, the KS-entropy, and the study of the unique properties of Anosov and Smale systems, Sinai billiards, strange attractors, etc. becomes clear. Many of these results are being used successfully in a number of branches of science, although the proper application of abstract mathematical results in a physical context sometimes requires significant effort. We (the present authors) have already applied some of these methods to certain problems of galactic dynamics and quantum cosmology, in the latter context while studying the properties of Wheeler-DeWitt superspace.

This volume represents an attempt to achieve a consistent geometrical treatment of observational cosmology from the concepts of the theory of dynamical systems. Since this mathematical technique is not yet a familiar tool in this field, after some doubts concerning the level of detail, we decided to begin with a summary of the elementary ideas of differential geometry, ergodic theory and catastrophe theory, confining ourselves to the main concepts and notations required in our applications here. At the end of each chapter we mention the main books and review articles where more detailed references can be found; in certain cases we refer to basic original papers as well.

We clearly realize the large responsibility we are assuming by introducing unfamiliar techniques in a subject in its phase of active development and acknowledge the inevitability that numerous points will arise requiring further analysis. At the same time, the approach itself has in part determined the basic problems on which we concentrate, while their further extent associated with particular theories of the origin and evolution of the large-scale Universe seems natural.

The main advantage of such a unified approach is the opportunity to consider the possibility of embracing a wide range of, at first sight, very different phenomena within the same physical framework, thus discovering their underlying universal properties.

We do hope that the problems considered here can serve as good examples which demonstrate not only the power but also the beauty of this abstract mathematical technique and stimulate its use in other areas of astrophysics and cosmology.

ACKNOWLEDGEMENTS

At the Matenadaran, the Institute of Ancient Manuscripts in Yerevan, an Armenian manuscript from the distant past is being kept with the following touching inscription appended at its end by the author of olden days:

"I thank the person who brought wood for me this severe winter when I was writing this folio."

We are happy to express our deep gratitude to the many persons who "brought wood" for us, among them mathematicians, physicists, and astronomers.

Our thanks go to Sergei Matinyan and especially George Savvidy, who have initiated our interest in ergodic theory. Our contacts with Dmitri Anosov, Vladimir Arnold and Yakov Pesin enabled us to keep in touch with current achievements in that area of mathematics. The regular contact over the years with Yakov Zeldovich and his collaborators has largely determined our taste in cosmology, while discussions with Victor Ambartsumian were very stimulating at all stages of our research. Remo Ruffini has kindly provided us with the opportunity to spend very valuable time at the International Center for Relativistic Astrophysics in Rome. *The Vatican Study Week* volume, a precious gift from the Reverend George Coyne, has stimulated our interest in large-scale cosmology in an essential way. We record the helpful discussions on different issues of this book with Guido Chincarini, Daniel Gerbal, Fabio Mardirossian, Joe Monaghan, Ilya Prigogine, Eduardo Salvador-Sole, Dennis Sciama and our collaborators, Vahram Harutyunyan and Artashes Petrosian. Thom Buchert, Thom Broadhurst, Valerie de Lapparent, Jerry Graham, John Huchra, Francesco Melchiorri, Manolis Plionis and George Smoot helped us by supplying illustrations or permitting the use of already published ones.

Finally we mention the great pleasure we had in our joint work with Robert Jantzen during his difficult task of editing the book. We ourselves are responsible, however, for all the remaining errors.

GLOSSARY

Geometry

$\forall$	for all
$\exists$	exists
$\in$	belongs to
$\cup$	unification of sets
$\cap$	intersection of sets
$\subset$	subset
$\preceq$	less or of the same order
R^n	Euclidean n-space
π	natural projection
A, B	atlases
M	manifold
$\mathcal{F}M$	smooth functions
TM	space of tangential vectors
T^*M	space of 1-forms
∇	connection
$Riem$	Riemann tensor
Ric	Ricci tensor
R	scalar curvature
To	torsion tensor
g	metric
$\otimes$	tensor product
C_j^i	contraction of tensors
K	two-dimensional curvature

Dynamical Systems

λ	Lyapunov characteristic exponents
μ	measure
$\bigvee$	smallest σ-algebra of partitions
ξ	partition
$h(T,\xi)$	entropy of partition ξ
$h(T)$	Kolmogorov-Sinai (KS) entropy
$b(t)$	time correlation function
dim_H	Hausdorff dimension
D_0	Kolmogorov capacity
D_1	information dimension
D_2	correlation dimension
D_q	Renyi dimensions

Cosmology

G	Einstein tensor
T	energy-momentum tensor
a	scale parameter of the Friedmannian Universe
η	conformal time parameter
ℓ	homogeneity scale
$\xi(r)$	spatial correlation function
$\omega(\theta)$	angular correlation function
$\zeta(R)$	correlation function in (x,v) 6-space
$\delta(z)$	perturbations at redshift z
$\mathcal{P}$	boundness function
Σ	multifunction of bound tree diagram

Chapter 1

THE PROBLEM OF THE LARGE-SCALE STRUCTURE OF THE UNIVERSE

In nature's infinite book of secrets
A little I can read.
William Shakespeare
("Anthony and Cleopatra")

1.1 Outlook of Main Issues

One hundred years ago astronomy almost exclusively dealt with the Sun, the Moon and the planets. Fifty years ago the main objects of interest became the stars, and thirty years ago, the galaxies. Today the frontiers are being moved outward to a new and intriguing area of investigation, the large scale structure of the Universe.

Determined mostly by the advances of observational technique, each of these fields was not only a carrier of new epistemological paradigms and moved the boundaries of common understanding, but also cast a powerful spell upon the formulation and development of new physical concepts and theories, and analytical and numerical methods. One is reminded of such elegant disciplines as celestial mechanics, itself having had tremendous influence on a number of branches of physics and mathematics, the theory of radiative transfer, the invariance principle, etc.

1

There is every reason to believe that the outstanding observational discoveries of recent decades concerning the distribution of matter in the Universe can also have their own specific mathematical treatment. This hope is particularly supported by the fact that the newly discovered features of the observed Universe, including the existence of giant coherent structures and voids, large-scale motions, the fractal nature of clustering, etc., were not predicted by any theory or scenario of the evolution of the early Universe. The appearance of new paradigms with a more contemporary point of view clearly seems natural. Moreover, in our opinion, to reveal these paradigms, in addition to the approach of the conventional theories and models (various type of initial density fluctuations, Zeldovich pancakes, dark matter of different natures and amounts, explosions, cosmic strings, etc.) one has to essentially proceed from the observational data together with certain fundamental physical laws which are still considered necessarily valid.

To investigate the problem of the large-scale structure of the Universe we will proceed based on the following assumptions following directly from observations:

1. The building blocks of the matter distribution are galaxies.

2. The dynamics of systems of galaxies is governed by Newtonian gravity.

3. These systems participate in the Hubble expansion.

4. The Universe is homogeneous at large enough scales.

Since one has no serious reason to doubt that General Relativity and its limit, the Newtonian law of gravity, are appropriate for the description of the dynamics of galactic clusters, only the homogeneity of the Universe remains as a subject for polemics. Suggested originally by Einstein in 1917 this assumption has actually become one of the basic points of modern cosmology. This idea, however, is not trivial at all, since the amount of observational information has increased enormously since the early work of Einstein, and by now has created certain challenges to that assumption. The latter is especially true concerning the distribution of extragalactic objects at large distances. However, the fundamental experimental fact in favor of homogeneity is the high degree of isotropy of the Cosmic Microwave Background Radiation (CMB). Presumably, this property of the CMB may carry more information about the global features of the space-time than we are presently able to appreciate. The inevitable unity of the large scale dynamics of the matter and the properties of the CMB dictates the necessity of considering these phenomena on the same footing.

However, even though these basic assumptions seem to be rather reliable, it is important to note that the study of the internal dynamics of systems of galaxies which we perform below remains valid independent of whether or not the Universe is homogeneous on large scales. At first sight this problem of galactic dynamics seems to coincide with one from a well-developed discipline also dealing with gravitating N-body systems, namely stellar dynamics. Why then cannot the methods developed for the latter problem be equally as useful for the investigation of clusters of galaxies?

Compare the typical parameters of stellar systems and those of galactic ones: the number of objects (stars) is $10^5 - 10^6$ in globular clusters and $10^{10} - 10^{12}$ in elliptical galaxies, while groups of galaxies contain $10 - 30$, and clusters of galaxies $10^2 - 10^3$ objects (Figure 1). All observations indicate the relaxed, quasi-equilibrium state of the stellar systems, very consistent with the estimates of N-body relaxation time scales. Therefore one can easily apply to them in the limit of large N the methods of equilibrium statistical mechanics and thermodynamics.

On the other hand both the observational data and estimates of a relaxation time far exceeding the Hubble time indicate that except from some dense regions of rich clusters, the typical groups and clusters of galaxies remain in an unrelaxed, far from equilibrium state. Consequently, for thse objects one needs not only to move to the dynamics of non-equilibrium systems, but very basic terms such as "bound system" trivially defined in stellar dynamics by means of the sign of the total energy, need serious reconsideration here.

Similar problems arise with the interpretation of observational data. Indeed, while the identification of a galaxy or globular cluster in the sky is typically not a great problem, the determination of groups, clusters and superclusters is usually based on subjectively chosen spatial, morphological and other empirical criteria. The latter properties become the basis for the creation of a number of catalogues and samples which serve as the main source for further studies. Moreover the inclusion or exclusion of a single galaxy with respect to the given group or cluster can sometimes have crucial consequences for further theoretical speculations.

Thus we arrive at our first issue:

> *To find a rigorous description of a cluster of galaxies as a system of gravitationally interacting objects.*

Note also that the long range character of the gravitational interaction in contrast with the electromagnetic one ensures gravitational interaction at any distance within the N-body system. Proper definitions of "bound" and "unbound" systems should therefore reflect this crucial difference.

a

b

c

Figure 1 *a) Globular cluster M3,*
b) giant elliptical galaxy M87;
c) remote cluster of galaxies CL 0939+4713 at z = 0.4 by Hubble Space
Telescope (NASA photo, credit Alan Dressler).

Now turn to the information which is derived directly from observations of clusters of galaxies. The corresponding typical catalogues contain in particular the magnitudes, 2-coordinates (right ascension and declination, galactic longitude and latitude, supergalactic longitude and latitude) and the redshifts, indicating the line-of-sight velocities of galaxies. The latter include both the Hubble and peculiar velocities of the object. In certain cases additional information, for example, on the dimensions, distances, absolute luminosities or even the masses of the galaxies may be also obtained from infrared, X-ray and other surveys, since those parameters do depend on the value of the Hubble constant. These estimations are usually based on certain empirical relations – Faber-Jackson, Tully-Fisher, 7 Samurai's, Surface Brightness fluctuations (SBF), Luminosity – slope of Surface Brightness (for First Ranked cluster galaxies), etc. Overcoming the various biases, like the Malmquist bias, for example, is one of the main difficulties of these studies.

The second issue, therefore, can be formulated as follows:

> *To reconstruct the substructure of the distribution of galaxies, including the identification of groups and clusters, from the available limited observational information.*

The subclustering of the filaments has at least two direct cosmological consequences which are related to each other. First, in contrast with relaxed stellar systems which have largely forgotten their initial states, the present state of clusters of galaxies does contain certain information about the processes of their formation. Second, the physical parameters of clusters and the deviations of their large scale motions from the Hubble expansion, together with the properties of the CMB, should contain unique information regarding the present values of cosmological parameters and the global history of the early Universe.

Consequently the third issue arising naturally is:

> *To obtain cosmological information, including in particular the values of the main cosmological parameters from the clustering properties of the large-scale distribution of matter and Cosmic Microwave Background radiation.*

The attempt to construct a mathematical framework encompassing these issues is the goal of the present monograph. Before beginning, let us give a brief overview of the observational background of large-scale cosmology.

1.2 The Observations: A Bird's Eye View

In 1750 Thomas Wright suggested and in 1787 William Herschel established the membership of the Sun in a huge system of stars, the Milky Way Galaxy.

Although since then many authors including the great Immanuel Kant have proposed that the "nebulous stars" might be other "island universes", only in the late 1920's did the existence of an extragalactic world become a physical reality. The subsequent surveys involving larger and larger distances created the amazing picture of the large scale Universe, thus confirming the quite common place of our Galaxy in it.

The Milky Way Galaxy was shown to be a member of a group of galaxies, also including another giant spiral, the Andromeda galaxy, along with more than 30 other galaxies. At the time when Hubble introduced the name "Local Group", only 13 members were known. One should anticipate the existence of as yet undiscovered members, especially in the direction of the Galactic disk, obscured due to strong absorption. Though the Local Group is one of the best studied systems of galaxies, there are uncertainties concerning the membership of already known galaxies. We shall discuss this problem in Chapter 4 in the framework of a rigorous formulation of an interacting system.

The Local Group is a part of a larger conglomerate of galactic systems, the Local Supercluster, centered in the Virgo cluster and including also those of Coma and Ursa Major. A region of low galactic density, the so-called Local void which is 20 Mpc in diameter, extends in the vicinity of the Local Group. (Here and below the distance scale is given based on the value $H = 75$km/s Mpc of the Hubble constant.)

We also mention the crucial information already gathered on clusters of galaxies from X-ray observations, including the indications of hot intergalactic gas in the form of sharply peaked profiles of the X-ray surface brightness at the centres of the clusters.

On larger scales the surveys reveal the existence of giant voids of diameter 20–50Mpc with sufficiently lower number density with respect to the mean, along with a definite sheet-like character of their bounding walls. One of the sheet-like structures, the Great Wall shown in Figure 2, extends at least 170Mpc and presumably has a continuation in the form of the Perseus-Pisces chain (Figure 3). According to estimates by Geller and Huchra the mass of the Great Wall could be at least $2 \cdot 10^{16} M_\odot$, exceeding the mass of the Local Supercluster by an order of magnitude.

A striking quantitative measure of the distribution of matter is given by the one-parameter representation of the two-point correlation functions.

For galaxies one has

$$\xi_{gg} = (r/r_0)^{-\gamma},$$

where r_0 is the correlation length $r_0 \simeq 5.4 \pm 1$Mpc and

$$\gamma \simeq 1.8,$$

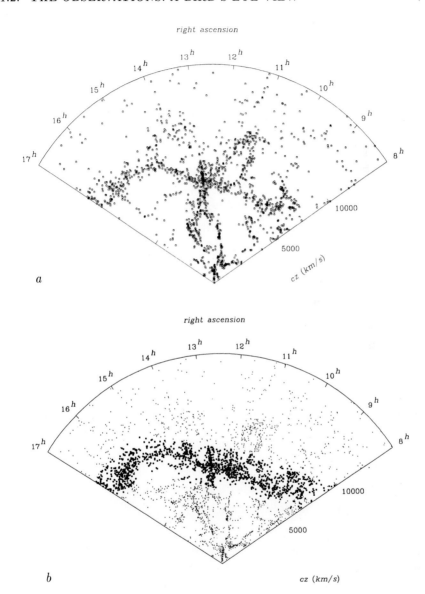

Figure 2 *a) Great Wall on a cone diagram containing 1761 galaxies with $m_{B(0)} \leq 15.5$ within the declination range $26°.5 < \delta < 38°.5$ (from V. de Lapparent, M. Geller and J. Huchra, Astrophys. J., vol.332, p.44, 1988).*

b) The Great Wall with 1622 galaxies highlighted. (from A. Zabludoff, M. Geller, J. Huchra and M. Ramella, preprint, 1993).

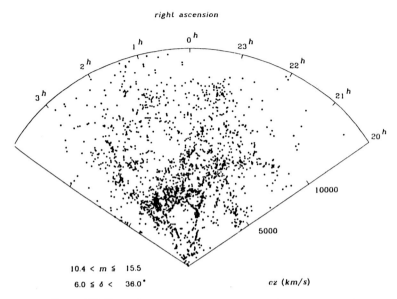

Figure 3 *Great Wall and Perseus-Pisces chain (from M. Geller and J. Huchra, Science, vol.246, p.897, 1989).*

a relation holding over scales from 10Kpc up to 10Mpc. There are indications of a galaxy-galaxy correlation on larger scales presumably with a different power index.

A cluster-cluster correlation is found with the same power index:

$$\xi_{cc} = (r/r_0)^{-\gamma},$$

but different correlation amplitudes depending on the richness of the cluster (as well as the correlation length). These scaling properties are often interpreted as evidence of a fractal distribution of the matter with Hausdorff dimension $\dim_H = 3 - \gamma$.

No less dramatic is the situation concerning the dynamical data on the filaments. A rather complicated velocity field already has been found in the neighborhood of the Local Group of galaxies. There is evidence not only of a definite Virgocentric flow in which the Local Group participates, but of an even stronger stream towards the Hydra-Centaurus supercluster.

The study of various samples of galaxies seems to strongly indicate large scale coherent motions deviating from the Hubble expansion. One such velocity anomaly if caused by gravitational interaction is attributed to the so-called Great Attractor located at a distance of 40Mpc with coordinates $l = 310°, b = 9°$ (Figure 4). As mentioned above the Local Group is also

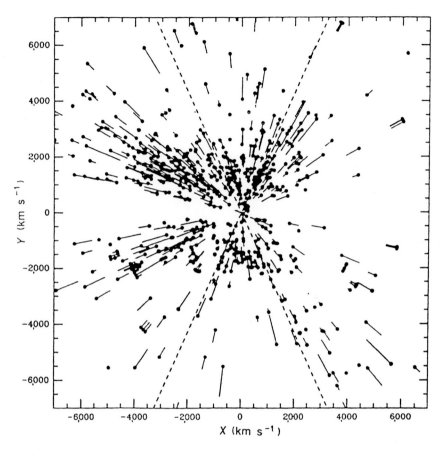

Figure 4 *Map of peculiar velocities of galaxies in the direction of the Great Attractor (from A. Dressler, Nature, vol.350, p.391, 1991). The lengths of vectors indicate the magnitudes of velocities.*

thought to be attracted by it. There is an evidence for even further attraction by the Shapley concentration (Giant Attractor) at a distance about 180Mpc.

Observational data seem to indicate that the velocity deviations of clusters of galaxies from the Hubble flow are the typical feature of large-scale motions. In principle from this fact one can assume the existence of three types of dark matter, one which is responsible for the flat rotation curves of the galaxies, another which can make the mean density of the Universe equal to the critical density ($\Omega = 1$), and a third one which creates the deviations from Hubble flow. To what degree these three types of dark matter may be interrelated or not remains to be understood in the future.

The most straightforward description of the hierarchy of motions in which we participate is with respect to the Cosmic Microwave Background Radiation as the absolute frame of rest. The high degree of isotropy of the CMB provides a unique possibility to measure the distortion of the temperature in the dipole approximation

$$\delta T/T = (v/c)\cos\theta + (v^2/2c^2)\cos 2\theta + O(v^3/c^3),$$

when the observer's velocity satisfies $v \ll c$; the first term on the right hand side is the dipole term, while the second is the quadrupole term.

Strong evidence of dipole anisotropy has been indicated by the Cosmic Background Explorer (COBE) (Figure 5) space measurements (Figure 6). As reported by Smoot at the XXI General Assembly of the IAU in Buenos-Aires in July 1991, the results reveal an Earth motion with speed:

$$v/c = 0.00122 \pm 0.00006,$$

or

$$v = 365 \pm 18 \text{km/s},$$

if the distortion of the blackbody temperature is due to the Doppler effect. The dipole is directed toward

$$l = 265°, \ b = 48°.$$

This measurement enables one to complete the following hierarchy of relative motions (Figure 7):

a) Earth relative to the Sun

$$v = 20\text{km/s}, \ l = 57°, \ b = 23°;$$

b) Earth relative to the center of the Galaxy

$$v = 220\text{km/s}, \ l = 90°, \ b = 0°;$$

c) Galaxy relative to the CMB

$$v = 550\text{km/s}, \ l = 266°, \ b = 30°;$$

d) Sun relative to the Local Group

$$v = 308\text{km/s}, \ l = 107°, \ b = -7°;$$

e) Local Group relative to the CMB

$$v = 620\text{km/s}, \ l = 277°, \ b = 30°.$$

The other, presumably more important aspect of the CMB measurements is determined by the role of the CMB as a carrier of unique information on the early epoch of the evolution of the Universe. This aspect concerns the spectrum and isotropy properties of the CMB on different angular scales (Figure 8). The measurements report a 10 percent accuracy fit of the observed spectrum by a Planckian one of temperature

$$T_0 = 2.736 \pm 0.017°K.$$

Estimates of the temperature of the CMB from the observations of the emission of rotational excited interstellar CN agree completely with this value.

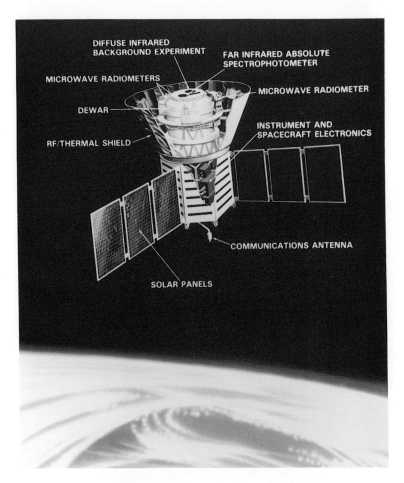

Figure 5 *Main devices of COBE.*

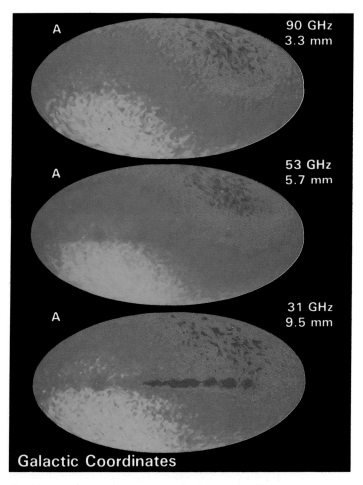

Figure 6 *The dipole anisotropy clearly seen on COBE full sky maps at three frequencies. The independence of the effect on frequency is noticeable.*

These results also mean that the temperature of the CMB is really the same if measured far from Earth.

The analysis of the results of first-year measurements by Differential Microwave Radiometers (DMR) on board COBE revealed the evidence of anisotropy with the root-mean-square (rms) value:

$$(\delta T/T) = 1.1 \cdot 10^{-5},$$

at angular scales: $> 10°$. The amplitude of the detected quadrupole signal was:

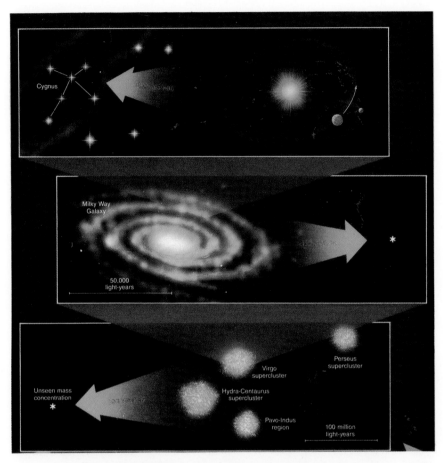

Figure 7 *Hierarchy of motions in which we participate (by S. Simpson, Sky and Telescope. © 1987 Sky Publishing Corp. Reproduced with permission).*

$$(\delta T/T)_Q = 5 \cdot 10^{-6}.$$

This remarkable discovery announced by Smoot in April 1992 and awaited for several decades (Figure 9) was shortly thereafter confirmed by other measurements.

Undoubtedly, the accuracy of the observational data presented above should be improved in the near future, and we give them here mainly for illustrative purposes. However, already they seem to provide enough of a basis to consider *the hierarchical matter distribution and highly smooth relic radiation as the observational paradigms of large-scale cosmology.*

a

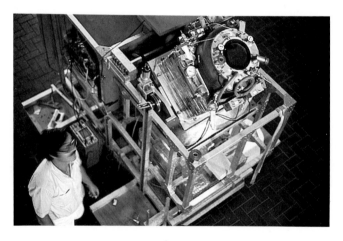

b

Figure 8 *Detectors of balloon experiments performed by group of Francesco Melchiorri and Paolo de Bernardis of University of Rome to study the anisotropy of the Cosmic Background Radiation:*

a) ARGO, at angular scale of $1°$ in the $500--3000\mu m$ range; anisotropies at a level $2 \cdot 10^{-5}$ had been detected during August, 1993 flight of ARGO.

b) ULISSE, at scale $6°$, in same wavelength range.

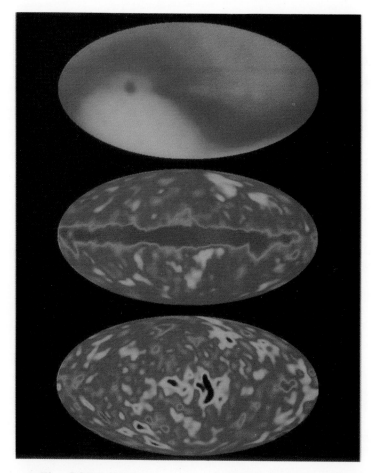

Figure 9 *The COBE-DMR sky maps: a) dipole anisotropy; b) map with extracted dipole anisotropy; the Galaxy disk emission is clearly seen; c) the contribution of noise.*

Bibliography

Reviews on practically all aspects of observational cosmology can be found in:

[1] Rubin V.C. and Coyne G.V. (Eds.), *Large-Scale Motions in the Universe: A Vatican Study Week*, Princeton University Press, Princeton, 1988.

[2] Blanchard A., Cernikier L., Lachieze-Rey M. and Tran Thanh Van J. (Eds.), *Physical Cosmology*, Editions Frontieres, 1991.

For an encyclopedic-like study covering the main contemporary theories see the book:

[3] Peebles P.J.E., *Principles of Physical Cosmology*, Princeton University Press, 1993.

Key items regarding the observational situation in the field are described in:

[4] Geller M.J., Huchra J.P., Mapping the Universe, *Science*, **246**, p.897, 1989.

[5] Dressler A., The Great Attractor: Do Galaxies Trace the Large-Scale Mass Distribution? *Nature*, **350**, p.391, 1991.

The COBE results are represented in:

[6] Mather J.C. et al, Measurement of the Cosmic Microwave Background Spectrum by the COBE FIRAS Instrument, *Ap .J .*, .420, 439, 1994.

[7] Smoot G.F. et al, Preliminary Results from COBE Differential Microwave Radiometers: Large Angular Scale Isotropy of the Cosmic Microwave Background, *Ap. J. Lett.*, **371**, p.L1, 1991.

[8] Smoot G.F. et al, Structure in the COBE Differential Microwave Radiometer First Year Maps, *Ap. J. Lett.*, **396**, p.L1, 1992.

Measurements of CMB temperature via rotational excitation of interstellar CN are described in:

[9] Roth K.C., Meyer D.M., Hawkins I., Interstellar Cyanogen and the Temperature of the Cosmic Microwave Background Radiation, *Ap. J. Lett.*, .413, p.L67, 1993.

Chapter 2

GEOMETRY, DYNAMICAL SYSTEMS, CATASTROPHES

> *Perhaps the imagination is on the verge of recovering its rights.*
> **Andre Breton**
> *"Manifeste du Surrealisme"*

The purpose of this section is to introduce the background ideas and notation of differential geometry and ergodic theory necessary for the understanding of the subsequent material. It is a self-contained presentation but in no way meant to be exhaustive.

2.1 Geometry

The first basic idea we will deal with throughout this monograph is that of a manifold.

A triplet $c = (U, \varphi, R^d)$ is called a chart on a set M, if $U \subset M$ and

$$\varphi : U \to V \subset R^d$$

is a 1–1 map onto (bijective) an open set V in R^d. Then U is the domain and d is the dimension of the chart c.

We will say that two charts $c = (U, \varphi, R^d)$ and $c' = (U', \varphi', R^d)$ are C^r-related $(r \geq 0)$ on M if:

M1. $\varphi(U \cap U')$ and $\varphi'(U \cap U')$ are open sets in R^d;

M2. $\varphi \circ \varphi'^{-1} : \varphi'(U \cap U') \to \varphi(U \cap U')$ and $\varphi' \circ \varphi^{-1} : \varphi(U \cap U') \to \varphi'(U \cap U')$ belong to $C^r(R^d)$.

The set of in pairs C^r-related charts is called a C^r-atlas of the set M if the union of the domains of all the charts is the set M. The atlases $\mathcal{A}$ and $\mathcal{B}$ of M are called C^r-related if $\mathcal{A} \cup \mathcal{B}$ is also an atlas of M. C^r-relation is an equivalence relation. The set M endowed with an equivalence class of atlases (C^r-structure) is called a manifold (Figures 10, 11). d is the dimension of M: $\dim M = d$.

A chart from the atlas of the set M is called a chart on the manifold M. If $\mathcal{A}$ is an atlas on M, then the set M endowed with the equivalence class of atlases containing $\mathcal{A}$ is called the manifold defined by the basis atlas $\mathcal{A}$.

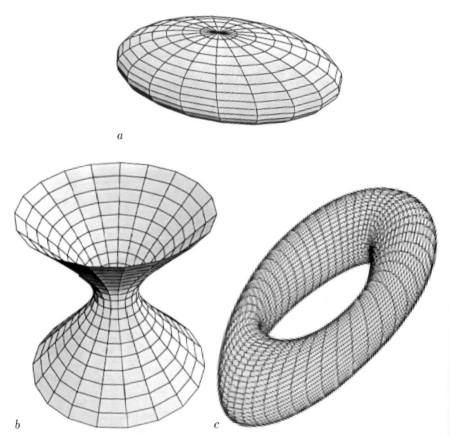

a

b   *c*

Figure 10 *Examples of manifolds.*

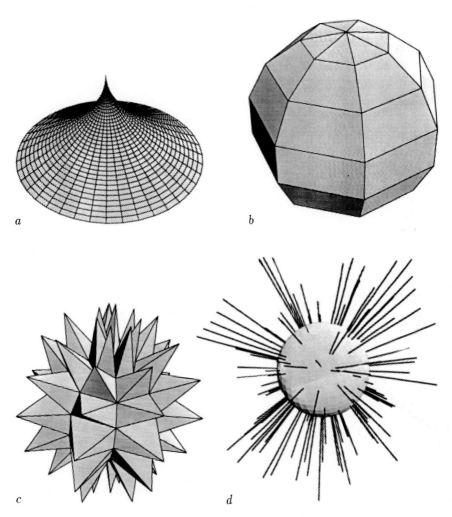

a

b

c

d

Figure 11 *Examples of non-manifolds.*

Let M be a manifold. One can give M a topology in a unique way such that for every chart $c = (U, \varphi, R^d)$ U is open, and φ is a topological isomorphism. This topology is said to underlie the manifold structure of M. Henceforth we will consider only manifolds with $r = \infty$ and an underlying Hausdorff topology (a topological space τ is called Hausdorff if whenever $x \in \tau$, $y \in \tau$, and $x \neq y$ then $\exists$ open sets U and V such that $x \in U$, $y \in V$, and $U \cap V = \emptyset$).

If $x^1, \ldots, x^d$ are maps from a set U of the manifold M into R, then $x = (x^1, \ldots, x^d)$ is called a coordinate system on M in U if (U, x, R^d) is a chart on M.

Differentiable map. If M and N are manifolds of dimensions d and n respectively, then the map

$$f : M \to N$$

is called smooth if for any chart (U, φ, R^d) of M and chart (V, ψ, R^n) of N the function

$$\psi \circ f \circ \varphi^{-1} : R^d \to R^n$$

is smooth, i.e., belongs to $C^\infty(R^d, R^n)$. The map $f : M \to N$ is a diffeomorphism if f is a bijective and f, f^{-1} are smooth.

Denote by $\mathcal{F}M$ the set of all differentiable real-valued functions defined on M:

$$\mathcal{F}M = \{f : M \to R \mid f \text{ is a smooth function}\}.$$

Operations of addition and multiplication by a real number can be defined for these functions: if $f, g \in \mathcal{F}M, \alpha \in R$ then, $\forall p \in M$

$$(f + g)(p) = f(p) + g(p),$$

$$(\alpha \cdot f)(p) = \alpha \cdot f(p) .$$

Endowed with these operations $\mathcal{F}M$ becomes a linear space. Moreover, the product of functions is defined as well

$$(f \cdot g)(p) = f(p) \cdot g(p)$$

making $\mathcal{F}M$ an Abelian algebra.

Tangent vector and tangent space. Let M be a d-dimensional manifold and $p \in M$. The map

$$\mathbf{v} : \mathcal{F}M \to R$$

is called a tangent vector to M at the point p if

V1. $\mathbf{v}(\alpha \cdot f + \beta \cdot g) = \alpha \cdot \mathbf{v}(f) + \beta \cdot \mathbf{v}(g) ,$

V2. $\mathbf{v}(f \cdot g) = \mathbf{v}(f) \cdot g(p) + f(p) \cdot \mathbf{v}(g) ,$

where $\alpha, \beta \in R$; $f, g \in \mathcal{F}M$. p is the base point to which $\mathbf{v}$ is attached. Hence the tangent vector to M at a point p due to condition **V1** is a linear functional on the linear space $\mathcal{F}M$, possessing also the derivation property **V2**.

If one again defines the operations of addition and multiplication by a real number for the tangent vectors at a point

$$(\alpha\mathbf{v} + \beta\mathbf{u})(f) = \alpha\mathbf{v}(f) + \beta\mathbf{u}(f),$$

where $\alpha, \beta \in R$; $\mathbf{u}, \mathbf{v}$ are tangent vectors, then the set of all tangent vectors at $p \in M$ denoted by T_pM will be a vector space called the tangent space to M at p.

The definition of the tangent vector can also be explained as follows. Let M be a d-dimensional manifold, and let $\lambda : I \to M$ be a smooth curve, with $0 \in I \subset R$ and I an open set in R. Assuming $\lambda(0) = p$, we define the map $\dot{\lambda}(0) : \mathcal{F}M \to R$ on $\mathcal{F}M$ by

$$\dot{\lambda}(0)(f) \equiv \lim_{s \to 0} \frac{1}{s} [f(\lambda(s)) - f(\lambda(0))] \ .$$

We will say that two curves λ and σ are equivalent if $\dot{\lambda}(0) = \dot{\sigma}(0)$; this is an equivalence relation on the set of all curves passing through the point p. Denote the equivalence class containing λ by $\mathbf{v}$. The tangent vector $\mathbf{v}$ at p may be defined as the action on smooth functions of this equivalence class, corresponding to the set of all mutually tangent curves passing through the point p (Figure 12). It is easy to see that these two definitions determine the same object, a tangent vector.

Given a point $p \in M$ consider a chart (U, x, R^d) on M so that $p \in U$. Special tangent vectors $\frac{\partial}{\partial x^a}|_p$ $(a = 1, \ldots, d)$ at a point p are defined by

$$\frac{\partial}{\partial x^a}|_p f = D_a(f \circ x^{-1})|_{x(p)},$$

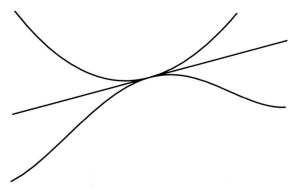

Figure 12 *Equivalent curves.*

where D_a denotes the partial derivative with respect to x^a in R^d. Then any tangent vector $\mathbf{v}$ from T_pM is uniquely represented as $v^a \frac{\partial}{\partial x^a}|_p$ where $v^a = \mathbf{v}(x^a)$. Therefore the tangent vectors $\frac{\partial}{\partial x^a}|_p$ can be considered to be a basis for the tangent space T_pM. Hence

$$\dim T_pM = \dim M = d.$$

Consider any basis $\{\mathbf{e}_a\}$ in T_pM. Any vector $\mathbf{v} \in T_pM$ can be uniquely represented in the form $\mathbf{v} = v^a \mathbf{e}_a$, where the numbers v^a denote the coordinates of the vector $\mathbf{v}$ with respect to the basis $\mathbf{e}_a$.

1-*form*. A real linear functional ω:

$$\omega : T_pM \to R : \mathbf{v} \mapsto \langle \omega, \mathbf{v} \rangle$$

is called a differential 1-form or just 1-form. The set of all 1-forms at a point p is denoted by T_p^*M. Analogously, when the basic operations for 1-forms and real numbers are defined by

$$\langle \alpha\omega + \beta\sigma, \mathbf{v} \rangle = \alpha \langle \omega, \mathbf{v} \rangle + \beta \langle \sigma, \mathbf{v} \rangle$$

for all $\alpha, \beta \in R$; $\omega, \sigma \in T_p^*M$, then T_p^*M becomes a linear space of dimension $\dim T_p^*M = d$.

One can also choose a basis of 1-forms $\{\mathbf{e}^a\}$ in T_p^*M, such that

$$\omega = \omega_a \mathbf{e}^a$$

and define two bases $\{\mathbf{e}_a\}$ and $\{\mathbf{e}^a\}$ for T_pM and T_p^*M, respectively, to be dual to each other if

$$\langle \mathbf{e}^a, \mathbf{e}_b \rangle = \delta^a{}_b = \begin{cases} 1 & a = b \ , \\ 0 & a \neq b \ . \end{cases}$$

Any $f \in \mathcal{F}M$ defines a 1-form $\mathbf{d}f$ at a point p in the following way

$$\langle \mathbf{d}f, \mathbf{v} \rangle = \mathbf{v}(f) \ ,$$

for all $\mathbf{v} \in T_pM$. $\mathbf{d}f$ is called the differential of f. If (U, x, R^d) is a chart on M, then the set of 1-forms $\{\mathbf{d}x^a\}$ is a basis of T_p^*M and is dual to the basis $\{\frac{\partial}{\partial x^a}\}$, since

$$\langle \mathbf{d}x^a, \frac{\partial}{\partial x^b} \rangle = \delta^a{}_b.$$

In that basis $\mathbf{d}f$ can be written as

$$\mathbf{d}f = \frac{\partial f}{\partial x^a}\mathbf{d}x^a \ .$$

Tensor. Construct the following cartesian product of spaces

$$\Pi_r^s = \underbrace{T_p^* M \times \cdots \times T_p^* M}_{r} \times \underbrace{T_p M \times \cdots \times T_p M}_{s} \ .$$

A multilinear functional

$$T : \Pi_r^s \to R$$

is called a tensor of type (r, s) at the point p. The set of all such tensors is called a tensor product space

$$T_s^r M_p = \underbrace{T_p M \otimes \ldots \otimes T_p M}_{r} \otimes \underbrace{T_p^* M \otimes \ldots \otimes T_p^* M}_{s} \ .$$

As special cases one has $T_0^1 M_p = T_p M$ and $T_1^0 M_p = T_p^* M$.

The sum and product by real numbers of tensors are defined in a natural way by

$$(\alpha T + \beta S)(\omega^1, \ldots, \omega^r, \mathbf{v}_1, \ldots, \mathbf{v}_s)$$
$$= \alpha T(\omega^1, \ldots, \omega^r, \mathbf{v}_1, \ldots, \mathbf{v}_s) + \beta S(\omega^1, \ldots, \omega^r, \mathbf{v}_1, \ldots, \mathbf{v}_s).$$

for all $\alpha, \beta \in R$; $T, S \in T_s^r M_p$. In view of these operations the tensor product space $T_s^r M_p$ becomes a d^{r+s}-dimensional linear space.

If $\mathbf{v}_a \in T_p M (a = 1, \ldots, r)$ and $\omega^b \in T_p^* M (b = 1, \ldots, s)$, then the tensor product of $\mathbf{v}$'s and ω's is the tensor

$$\mathbf{v}_1 \otimes \cdots \otimes \mathbf{v}_r \otimes \omega^1 \otimes \cdots \otimes \omega^s \in T_s^r M_p$$

defined by

$$\mathbf{v}_1 \otimes \cdots \otimes \mathbf{v}_r \otimes \omega^1 \otimes \cdots \otimes \omega^s(\sigma^1, \ldots, \sigma^r, \mathbf{u}_1, \ldots, \mathbf{u}_s) = \langle \sigma^1, \mathbf{v}_1 \rangle \cdots \langle \omega^s, \mathbf{u}_s \rangle.$$

Similarly, if $T \in T_s^r M_p$, $S \in T_n^m M_p$ then their outer product $T \otimes S \in T_{s+n}^{r+m} M_p$ is defined by

$$T \otimes S(\sigma^1, \ldots, \sigma^{r+m}, \mathbf{u}_1, \ldots, \mathbf{u}_{s+n})$$
$$= T(\sigma^1, \ldots, \sigma^r, \mathbf{u}_1, \ldots, \mathbf{u}_s) \cdot S(\sigma^{r+1}, \ldots, \sigma^{r+m}, \mathbf{u}_{s+1}, \ldots, \mathbf{u}_{s+n}) \ .$$

If $\{\mathbf{e}_a\}$ and $\{\mathbf{e}^b\}$ are dual bases respectively in T_pM and T_p^*M, then

$$\{\mathbf{e}_{a_1} \otimes \cdots \otimes \mathbf{e}_{a_r} \otimes \mathbf{e}^{b_1} \otimes \cdots \otimes \mathbf{e}^{b_s}\} \quad a_i, b_i = 1, \ldots, d$$

is a basis of $T_s^r M_p$.

Any tensor T in $T_s^r M_p$ can be uniquely represented in that basis by means of the following expression

$$T = T^{a_1 \ldots a_r}{}_{b_1 \ldots b_s} \mathbf{e}_{a_1} \otimes \cdots \otimes \mathbf{e}_{a_r} \otimes \mathbf{e}^{b_1} \otimes \cdots \otimes \mathbf{e}^{b_s},$$

where $T^{a_1 \ldots a_r}{}_{b_1 \ldots b_s}$ are the components of T with respect to dual bases $\{\mathbf{e}_a\}$, $\{\mathbf{e}^b\}$:

$$T^{a_1 \ldots a_r}{}_{b_1 \ldots b_s} = T(\mathbf{e}^{a_1}, \ldots, \mathbf{e}^{a_r}, \mathbf{e}_{b_1}, \ldots, \mathbf{e}_{b_s}) \ .$$

Finally define the contraction of a tensor $T \in T_s^r M_p$ by

$$C_j^i T(\cdot) = T(\ldots, \overset{i}{\mathbf{e}^a}, \ldots; \ldots, \overset{j}{\mathbf{e}_a}, \ldots) \ ,$$

where $i \leq r$ and $j \leq s$.

Tensor field. So far we are dealing with tensors defined at a point. Now let us define tensor fields. Let $c = (U, x, R^d)$ be a chart on M. By means of its local coordinates $x = (x^1, \ldots, x^d)$, the vectors $\frac{\partial}{\partial x^a}|_p$, 1-forms $\mathbf{d}x^b|_p$, and type (r, s) basis tensors

$$\frac{\partial}{\partial x^{a_1}} \otimes \cdots \otimes \frac{\partial}{\partial x^{a_r}} \otimes \mathbf{d}x^{b_1} \otimes \cdots \otimes \mathbf{d}x^{b_s}$$

are defined at each point p of U. Such tensor bases are called coordinate ones.

We will say that a smooth (differentiable of class C^∞) type (r, s) tensor field T is defined on M if an element of $T_s^r M_p$ is defined at each point p of M, i.e.,

$$T : M \to \bigcup_{p \in M} T_s^r M_p : p \mapsto T(p) \in T_s^r M_p$$

such that the components of T are smooth functions with respect to all coordinate bases.

Next we consider the behavior of a tensor field at different points of the manifold. For example, in the case of a smooth vector field it is not yet clear what meaning to give an equation like $\mathbf{v}(p) = \mathbf{v}(q)$, where $\mathbf{v}$ is a smooth vector field and p, q are different points of M. One can only compare tangent vectors at the same point, so one must somehow propagate one of the tangent vectors parallel to itself (without change in some sense) along a curve connecting the two points p and q, in order to compare it with the other tangent vector at the second point. However, so far we have no notion of "propagation" associated with the definition of a manifold.

Thus one is forced to introduce the concept of a connection, which can be introduced more simply in terms of a derivative rather than a finite operation of transport. In order to keep a tangent vector unchanged during its propagation along a given curve, one should calculate the "derivative" of that vector field with respect to the tangent vector of the curve: when the derivative is zero the vector is said to be parallelly propagated along the curve. This new derivative is defined by the connection.

Connection ∇. Let M be a smooth manifold and $\mathcal{X}M$ the space of all smooth vector fields on M. A linear connection or covariant derivative on M is a map

$$\nabla : \mathcal{X}M \times \mathcal{X}M \to \mathcal{X}M : (X,Y) \mapsto \nabla_X Y$$

satisfying the following axioms

$\nabla 1.$ $\nabla_{fX+gY} Z = f \nabla_X Z + g \nabla_Y Z$,

$\nabla 2.$ $\nabla_X(\alpha Y + \beta Z) = \alpha \nabla_X Y + \beta \nabla_X Y$,

$\nabla 3.$ $\nabla_X fY = X(f)Y + f \nabla_X Y$,

where $f, g \in \mathcal{F}M$; $X, Y, Z \in \mathcal{X}M$; $\alpha, \beta \in R$. According to axiom $\nabla 1$, ∇ is a tensor in its first argument, but according to $\nabla 2$ and $\nabla 3$, is a derivative of its second argument. $\nabla 1$ enables one to consider the vector field ∇Y as $(1,1)$ tensor field whose evaluation on X in its first argument yields $\nabla_X Y$. Then $\nabla 2$ and $\nabla 3$ can be rewritten in the form

$\nabla 2.$ $\nabla(\alpha Y + \beta Z) = \alpha \nabla Y + \beta \nabla Y$,

$\nabla 3.$ $\nabla fY = \mathbf{d}f \otimes Y + f \nabla Y$.

The covariant derivative can be extended to tensor fields of any type by imposing the following conditions:

C1. If T is a type (r,s) tensor field, then ∇T is a type $(r, s+1)$ tensor field.

C2. ∇ is a linear operator (map) commuting with contraction

$$\nabla C_j^i = C_j^i \nabla, \quad \forall i \leq r \text{ and } \forall j \leq s .$$

C3. For any tensor fields T, S one has the derivation property (Leibniz rule)

$$\nabla(T \otimes S) = \nabla T \otimes S + T \otimes \nabla S ,$$

C4. $\nabla f = \mathbf{d}f \quad \forall f \in \mathcal{F}M .$

The covariant derivative defines parallel propagation in the following way. Let λ be a smooth curve with tangent vector field $X = \dot{\lambda}$, i.e. $\forall f \in \mathcal{F}M$

$$X_p f = X_{\lambda(s)} f = \dot{\lambda}(s) f = \lim_{h \to 0} \frac{1}{h} \left[f(\lambda(s + h)) - f(\lambda(s)) \right] ,$$

and T a tensor field defined along that curve. The covariant derivative $\nabla_X T$ of T along the curve λ is defined as $\nabla_X \hat{T}$, where X is the tangent to λ and $\hat{T}$ is a smooth tensor field extending T on an open set containing the curve. $\nabla_X T$ is a tensor field defined along the curve independent of the particular extension $\hat{T}$. The tensor T is parallel propagated along the curve λ when $\nabla_X T = 0$.

An important concept which will be used often in our work is that of a geodesic. A curve λ with tangent vector X satisfying the equation

$$\nabla_X X = 0 \tag{2.1}$$

is called a geodesic.

A number of important tensor fields accompany any connection. One of them, the curvature tensor, is a basic ingredient of almost all problems considered in this book (Figure 13).

The Riemann (curvature) $(1, 3)$ type tensor field *Riem* is defined by

$$Riem(X, Y)Z = ([\nabla_X, \nabla_Y] - \nabla_{[X,Y]})Z , \tag{2.2}$$

the Ricci $(0, 2)$ type tensor field by

$$Ric = C_2^1 Riem , \tag{2.3}$$

and the torsion $(0, 2)$ type tensor field To by

$$To(X, Y) = \nabla_X Y - \nabla_Y X - [X, Y] . \tag{2.4}$$

where $[X, Y] = XY - YX$ is also a vector field (the Lie bracket), while $[\nabla_X, \nabla_Y] = \nabla_X \nabla_Y - \nabla_Y \nabla_X$ is just the commutator of the two derivatives.

Metric. A $(0, 2)$ type tensor field g is called a metric tensor, if

g1. $g(X, Y) = g(Y, X)$, $\forall X, Y \in TM$ (symmetry) ,

g2. $\forall Y \in TM$, $g(X, Y) = 0 \Rightarrow X = 0$ (nondegeneracy).

When $g(X, X) > 0$ for all $X \neq 0$ (positive-definiteness) the metric is called Riemannian, otherwise pseudo-Riemannian.

The metric g attributes a length $\|X\| = |g(X, X)|^{1/2}$ to any vector X and defines the angle between two vectors

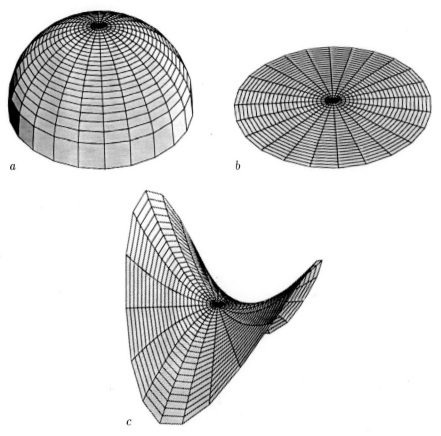

Figure 13 *Local geometries with different curvatures: a) Positive-curvature; b) Flat; c) Negative-curvature.*

$$\cos \angle(X,Y) = \frac{g(X,Y)}{\|X\| \cdot \|Y\|},$$

if $\|X\| \cdot \|Y\| \neq 0$. X and Y are called orthogonal if $g(X,Y) = 0$.

The metric g in a coordinate basis has the form

$$g = g_{ab}\mathbf{d}x^a \otimes \mathbf{d}x^b ,\qquad (2.5)$$

and defines uniquely an isomorphism from TM to T^*M

$$\imath : TM \to T^*M : X \mapsto \imath(X)$$

attributing $\omega \in T^*M$ to any $X \in TM$ so that

$$\langle \omega, Y \rangle = g(X, Y) \text{ for all } Y \in TM$$

i.e.

$$\imath(X) = \omega = g(X, \cdot) \, ,$$

where the centered dot in the argument of a tensor means that it is left unevaluated. A metric can be defined on T^*M:

$$g(\omega, \sigma) = g(\imath^{-1}(\omega), \imath^{-1}(\sigma)) \, ,$$

$$g = g^{ab} \frac{\partial}{\partial x^a} \otimes \frac{\partial}{\partial x^b},$$

where $g^{ac}g_{cb} = \delta^a{}_b$.

Using the metric tensor one can define the scalar curvature $R \in \mathcal{F}M$:

$$R = g^{ab} Ric_{ab} \equiv C_1^1 \circ \imath(Ric) \, . \tag{2.6}$$

A connection is called a Levi-Civita connection if

LC1. $To(X, Y) = 0$ (torsion free connection),

LC2. $\nabla g = 0$ (Riemannian connection).

For a given metric, the Levi-Civita connection is uniquely defined. When only the second condition is satisfied the connection is called a metric (Riemannian) one.

Jacobi equation. Given a metric connection, one can study the behavior of nearby geodesics. Suppose **u** is the unit tangent to a geodesic curve. One can then introduce a geodesic deviation vector **n** along the geodesic which is orthogonal to **u** and which represents the limiting behavior of the "separation vector" between the given geodesic and a nearby one. The vector **n** satisfies the equation of geodesic deviation

$$\nabla_{\mathbf{u}} \nabla_{\mathbf{u}} \mathbf{n} + Riem(\mathbf{n}, \mathbf{u})\mathbf{u} = 0 \, , \tag{2.7}$$

often called the Jacobi equation.

If one expresses this equation in a coordinate system it has the form

$$\ddot{n}^a + K^a{}_b n^b = 0 \, , \tag{2.8}$$

where the dot indicates the covariant derivative with respect to **u**,

$$K^a{}_b = Riem^u{}_{cbd} u^c u^d \ , \tag{2.9}$$

and $Riem^a{}_{cbd}$ are the coordinate components of the Riemann tensor.

2.2 Dynamical Systems

To illustrate what kind of problems the qualitative theory of dynamical systems deals with, let us consider a system which is of particular importance for us, namely a system of N particles in R^3 evolving according to certain equations of motion. In particular when the energy of the system is conserved, the motion in phase space is confined to the energy hypersurface and is described by Hamiltonian equations of motion for the coordinates q and momenta p:

$$\frac{dq^a}{dt} = \frac{\partial H}{\partial p_a} ,$$
$$\frac{dp_a}{dt} = -\frac{\partial H}{\partial q^a} , \tag{2.10}$$
$$p, q \in R^{3N} \ .$$

If the initial state (p_0, q_0) at time $t = 0$ is given, these equations determine the state $(p(t), q(t))$ of the Hamiltonian system at any time t, i.e., the evolutionary curve of the system in the phase space R^{6N}. One is thus led to the following transformation of the phase space:

$$f^t : \ R^{6N} \to R^{6N} : (p_0, q_0) \mapsto (p(t), q(t)) \ , \tag{2.11}$$

called the phase flow (Figure 14).

 A Hamiltonian system is an important type of dynamical system or "flow". A flow is an one-parameter group of transformations acting on some space M (called the phase space). In other words for any $t \in R$, a transformation f^t on the smooth manifold M

$$f^t : M \to M$$

is defined, and this family of transformations satisfies the conditions of a group

$$f^0 = id \ ,$$
$$f^{s+t} = f^s \circ f^t \ ,$$
$$f^{-t} = (f^t)^{-1} \ ,$$

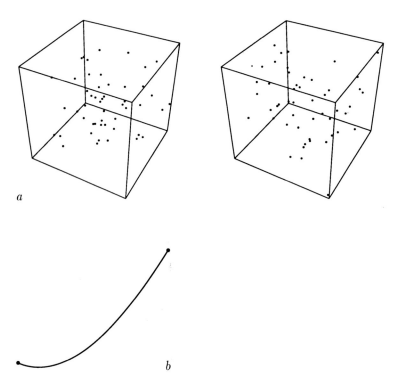

Figure 14   *Evolution in R^3 (a) and R^{6N} phase spaces (b).*

for arbitrary $t, s \in R$. For the Hamiltonian case the group parameter t labeling this family is the time variable.

A dynamical system or flow is smooth if the image point $f^t x$ depends smoothly on (t, x) and if the generating vector field

$$\mathbf{v}(x) = \frac{df^t x}{dt}\Big|_{t=0},$$

is a smooth vector field on M. If M is a compact smooth manifold then there always exists a smooth flow on it. The trajectories of the smooth flow can only be one of the following (Figure 15):

1. a regular curve diffeomorphic to R^1,

2. a point (equilibrium point),

3. a closed curve (periodic trajectory—diffeomorphic to the circle S^1) .

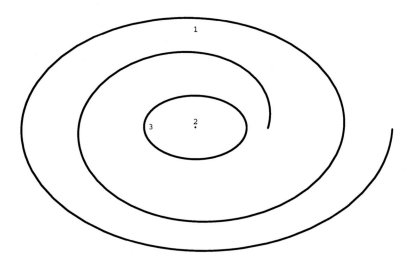

Figure 15 *Types of trajectories: 1) regular; 2) point; 3) circle.*

In the our Hamiltonian phase flow example with a time-independent Hamiltonian of the form

$$H(p,q) = \frac{1}{2}g^{ab}(q)p_a p_b + V(q) \ , \tag{2.12}$$

where $g = g_{ab}\mathbf{dq}^a \otimes \mathbf{dq}^b$ is a Riemannian metric on the configuration space of the variables q, the system point remains on the hypersurface of constant energy

$$H(p,q) = E \tag{2.13}$$

during its evolution in phase space. In this case the Maupertuis principle enables one to represent the phase flow of a Hamiltonian system as the geodesic flow in the region of the configuration space allowed by the energy constraint

$$Q = \{q \mid V(q) < E\} \tag{2.14}$$

associated with another Riemannian metric obtained by rescaling g

$$G = [E - V(q)]g \ . \tag{2.15}$$

The Hamiltonian equations with time as the parameter are then equivalent to the geodesic equations with respect to this metric G with the associated arclength s as the parameter

$$\nabla_{\mathbf{u}}\mathbf{u} = 0 \ , \tag{2.16}$$

where
$$ds = \sqrt{2}(E - V(q))dt \qquad (2.17)$$
is the differential relationship between the two different parametrizations of
the common trajectories in phase space and $\mathbf{u}$ is the tangent vector to the
geodesic. The energy condition $H(p, q) = E$ takes the form $G(\mathbf{u}, \mathbf{u}) = 1$
requiring the tangent vector $\mathbf{u}$ to be a unit vector.

Similar dynamical systems defined on manifolds with a natural measure
are investigated in ergodic theory. Several key concepts of that theory are
now described.

Let f be a smooth flow on a manifold M. Assume that a σ-field $\mathcal{B}(M)$ of
measurable sets of M and a measure P are defined on M. A smooth flow is
called measure-preserving if for any measurable set the following condition
holds
$$P(f^t A) = P(A), \ \forall A \in \mathcal{B}(M), \ \forall t \in R , \qquad (2.18)$$

i.e., if the set's measure is preserved under the flow. Liouville's theorem
states that the transformation (2.11) of the phase space R^{6N} of the Hamiltonian system (2.10) preserves the Lebesgue measure μ

$$\mu(A) = \int_A dq^1 \ldots dq^{3N} dp_1 \ldots dp_{3N} .$$

Therefore such a Hamiltonian flow is measure-preserving.

In order to describe the important concept of entropy let us consider a
partition of a manifold M with unit measure (i.e., $P(M) = 1$) into a number
of pairwise-disjoint measurable sets (Figure 16) $\xi = \{A_i\}$, $i \in I$, $A_i \in \mathcal{B}(M)$

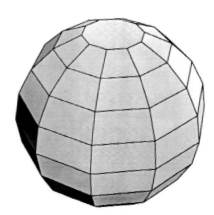

Figure 16 *A partition of a sphere.*

which cover the manifold

P1. $A_i \bigcap A_j = \emptyset$, if $i \neq j$,

P2. $\bigcup_{i \in I} A_i = M$.

The sets in the partition are called the atoms of the partition. We will introduce two operations with partitions.

Let

$$\xi = \{A_i\}$$

and

$$\eta = \{B_i\},$$

be partitions. We will say η is finer partition than ξ and write

$$\xi \leq \eta$$

if and only if each atom of ξ is a union of atoms from η.

For any set of partitions $\{\xi_i\}$, $i \in I$, two new partitions $\zeta = \bigvee_{i \in I} \xi_i$ and $\eta = \bigwedge_{i \in I} \xi_i$ may be introduced in the following way. The first

$$\zeta = \bigvee_{i \in I} \xi_i$$

is a finer partition constructed from the intersections of the atoms of the individual partitions, and is entirely defined by the following properties

V1. $\forall i \quad \xi_i \leq \zeta$,

V2. if $\quad \forall i, \ \xi_i \leq \zeta'$ then $\ \zeta \leq \zeta'$,

i.e.

$$\zeta = \inf\{\zeta' | \forall i \in I, \ \xi_i \leq \zeta'\} \ .$$

One can easily see that ζ is the collection of all sets of the form

$$\bigcap_{i \in I} A_i^{j_i}$$

where $A_i^{j_i}$ is an arbitrary atom of ξ_i (Figure 17).

The second

$$\eta = \bigwedge_{i \in I} \xi_i$$

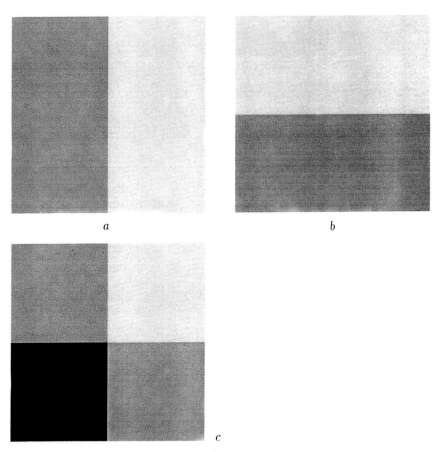

a b

c

Figure 17 *a)* $\xi = \{A_1, A_2\}$; *b)* $\eta = \{B_1, B_2\}$; *c)* $\xi \vee \eta$.

is entirely defined by the following properties

$\wedge$1. $\forall i$ $\eta \leq \xi_i$,

$\wedge$2. if $\forall i$, $\eta' \leq \xi_i$ then $\eta' \leq \eta$,

i.e.,

$$\eta = \sup\{\eta' | \forall i \in I, \ \eta' \leq \xi_i\} \ .$$

In other words every individual partition is finer than η, and unless their atoms have some special relationships, η will be the identity partition (Figure 18).

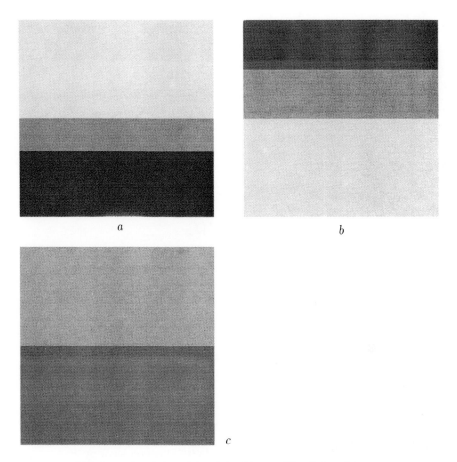

Figure 18 *a)* $\xi = \{A_1, A_2\}$; *b)* $\eta = \{B_1, B_2\}$; *c)* $\xi \wedge \eta$.

The Shennon entropy of the finite partition $\xi = \{A_i\}$, $i \in I = \{1, \ldots, k\}$ is defined by the following well known formula

$$H(\xi) = -\sum_{i=1}^{k} p(A_i) \ln p(A_i), \qquad (0 \ln 0 \equiv 0). \qquad (2.19)$$

Consider now the partition

$$\xi^n \equiv \bigvee_{i=0}^{n-1} f^{-i} \xi,$$

where f is a measure-preserving flow. We define the entropy of f with respect to ξ by

$$h(f,\xi) = \lim_{n \to \infty} \frac{1}{n} H(\xi^n) \, . \tag{2.20}$$

This limit does exist and has the bound $h(f,\xi) \leq \ln k$. The upper limit of $h(f,\xi)$ for finer and finer partitions is called the KS-entropy of f (after Kolmogorov and Sinai):

$$h(f) = \sup_{\xi}\{h(f,\xi)\} \, , \tag{2.21}$$

where the supremum extends over all finite partitions. The entropy satisfies the property:

$$h(f^t) = |t| h(f),$$

for any real t.

Ergodic theory classifies dynamical systems by various statistical properties. Weaker statistical properties characterize ergodic dynamical systems f which satisfy the condition

$$f^t A = A \Rightarrow P(A) = 0 \text{ or } P(A) = 1 \, , \tag{2.22}$$

i.e., any invariant set has zero or complete measure.

We will call a system chaotic if the system is ergodic and $h(f) > 0$, and a deterministic system if $h(f) = 0$. One can prove that the KS-entropy is zero for an integrable system.

Now we formulate a property of dynamical systems which is of particular importance for us. Consider an ergodic dynamical system f and a measurable partition ξ with k atoms and having finite Shennon entropy $H(\xi) < \infty$. Then there are at most

$$k^n = e^{n \ln k}$$

atoms in the partition ξ^n. If each of these atoms is to have equal measure, then the measure of each must be $e^{-n \ln k}$. One can prove that if $h(f,\xi) > 0$ then most of the phase space will be partitioned by about $e^{nh(f,\xi)}$ atoms each of whose measure is approximately $e^{-nh(f,\xi)}$ (Figure 19). This statement is usually called the equipartition property or equipartition theorem.

The statistical properties of dynamical systems can also be described by correlation functions. The latter are defined in the following way:

$$b_{g_1,g_2}(t) = \int_M g_1(f^t x) g_2(x) P(dx) - \int_M g_1(x) P(dx) \int_M g_2(x) P(dx), \tag{2.23}$$

where $g_1, g_2 \in L^2(M)$.

Figure 19 *Evolution of a partition.*

Systems for which

$$\lim_{t \to \infty} b_{g_1,g_2}(t) = 0 \tag{2.24}$$

are called mixing ones. The difference between mixing systems and systems which are only ergodic can be understood as follows (Figure 20). A mixing transformation f means that for any measurable sets A and B the sequence f^n becomes asymptotically independent:

$$\lim_{n \to \infty} P(f^{-n}A \cap B) = P(A)P(B) , \tag{2.25}$$

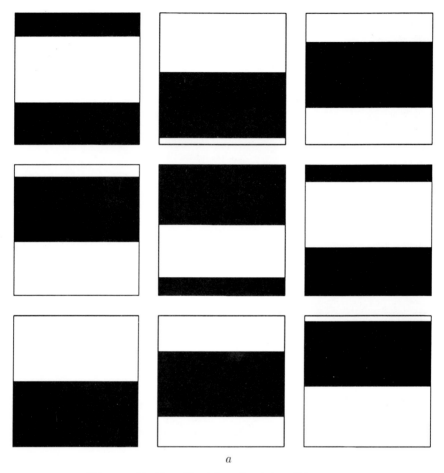

a

Figure 20 *Ergodic (a) and mixing (b) systems.*

where $A, B \in \mathcal{B}(M)$, and f is the invariant respect to the measure P:

$$P(A) = \int_A P(dx), \quad P(M) = 1 \ . \tag{2.26}$$

On the other hand ergodicity means that f becomes independent on the average, for each pair of sets:

$$\lim_{n \to \infty} \frac{1}{n} \sum_{i=0}^{n-1} P(f^{-i} A \cap B) = P(A)P(B). \tag{2.27}$$

b

Figure 20 *(Continued)*

Mixing systems cover uniformly the state space manifold M, with a rate determined by the rate of decrease of the correlation functions with respect to time. In ergodic theory different types of mixing are defined; weak mixing, pure mixing, n-fold mixing, as well as mixing characterizing systems with stronger statistical properties, namely K-systems and hyperbolic systems (Axiom A). For our purposes we mention only a result concerning the latter, namely that the correlation function decreases exponentially

$$\mid b(t) \mid < Ce^{-\beta ht} \tag{2.28}$$

where h is the KS-entropy.

Let us discuss K-systems in more detail. First we give the definition of the Tail-partition:

$$Tail(f,\xi) = \bigwedge_{n=0}^{+\infty} \bigvee_{i=n}^{+\infty} f^i \xi .$$

It can be considered as the collection of partitions in the infinitely distant future. A tail-partition is determined by each of the following ones:

$$\bigvee_{i=0}^{+\infty} f^i\xi, \quad \bigvee_{i=1}^{+\infty} f^i\xi, \ldots, \bigvee_{i=n}^{+\infty} f^i\xi, \ldots ,$$

i.e.

$$Tail(f,\xi) \leq \bigvee_{i=n}^{+\infty} f^i\xi ,$$

for any integer n.

The transformation f leads to a K-system if there exists an η-partition such that the following conditions are fulfilled:

$$\bigvee_{i=-\infty}^{+\infty} f^i \eta = \varepsilon ,$$

$$Tail(f,\eta) = \nu.$$

Here ε is a partition which contains all points of the state space M, and $\nu = \{M\}$. In other words the first condition means that the results of all possible experiments are determined by those of $f^i\eta$, $i \in (-\infty, +\infty)$. And the second one is the well known 0–1 Kolmogorov law, i.e., knowledge about the trajectory in the infinitely distant future gives no information about the actual trajectory of the system; it can distinguish either almost all trajectories (with measure 1) or almost no trajectories (with measure 0).

In the case of complete statistical independence of the events, i.e., when

$$P(A \cap f^n B) = P(A)P(B),$$

for all measurable sets A and B, where n is an integer, then the flow of the transformation f is a Bernoulli one.

2.3   Catastrophes

Catastrophe theory is a theory of the local behavior of typical smooth functions near critical points. It helps describe functions arising in certain physical phenomena whose precise physical laws are not known.

Suppose a family of real-valued functions V_c

$$V_c(x) = V(x,c) \, , \ x \in R^n, \ c \in R^k \, ,$$

is given, where $x \in R^n$ are generalized coordinates (state parameters) on which the functions depend, while the parameters $c \in R^k$ labeling the family are parameters (control parameters) which influence the qualitative properties of these functions. Catastrophe theory studies the behavior of the critical points of such functions while varying the control parameters c. Jump-like changes in their properties which occur during the smooth variation of c are called catastrophes.

The subset M of the space $R^n \times R^k$ for which

$$M = \{(x,c) \in R^n \times R^k \mid DV_c(x) = 0\} \, ,$$

i.e., the set of all critical points of the family of functions V_c, is called the space of catastrophes of V. The restriction to M of the natural projection onto the space of control parameters

$$\pi : R^n \times R^k \to R^k : (x,c) \mapsto c$$

is called the catastrophe map χ, i.e.

$$\chi = \pi|_M.$$

An important subset of M is the set S consisting of the singular points of the catastrophe map χ:

$$S = \{(x,c) \in M \mid \dim(\operatorname{range}(D\chi)) < k\} \, .$$

Another important set is its projection, the bifurcation set

$$B = \chi(S) \subset R^k \, . \tag{2.29}$$

The local properties of a function $V(x)$ or a family of functions $V(x,c)$ are determined by several theorems of functional analysis. First consider a function

$$V : R^1 \to R^1$$

at a non-critical point x

$$V'(x) \neq 0 \, .$$

From the implicit function theorem it follows that one can make a smooth change of coordinates

$$y = y(x)$$

so that

$$V \doteq y .$$

where the relational symbol $\doteq$ denotes "equals after smooth change of coordinates." At a critical point x for which the second derivative is nonzero

$$V'(x) = 0, \; V''(x) \neq 0 , \tag{2.30}$$

the Morse theorem states that

$$V \doteq y^2 .$$

Such points (2.30) are called non-degenerate or Morse critical points. They are the typical ones, i.e., all remaining cases are reduced to them under small changes of the function.

The situation is quite different if we are interested in a family of functions rather than in an individual one. It turns out that the degenerate cases

$$V' = V'' = 0$$

are no longer removable.

The classification of the types of critical points which can occur for typical smooth functions is dealt with by Thom's theorem. According to Thom's theorem, in the typical case the class of real-valued functions on R^n depending on k parameters is structurally stable and in the neighbourhood of a point such a function is equivalent to one of following functions:

Non-critical point: x_1;

Non-degenerate or Morse critical point: $x_1^2 + \cdots + x_i^2 - x_{i+1}^2 - \cdots - x_n^2$;

Degenerate critical point: one has the following elementary catastrophes (Figure 21):

1. Fold (A_2):

$$(1/3)x^3 + ax . \tag{2.31}$$

The critical points are determined by equation

$$V'(x,a) = x^2 + a = 0 .$$

The function when $a = 0$ has a non-Morse point ($V' = V'' = 0$) at $x = 0$; the point $a = 0$ is the bifurcation point or separatrix. It divides the space of control parameters (a straight line in this case) into regions where the functions have similar qualitative properties.

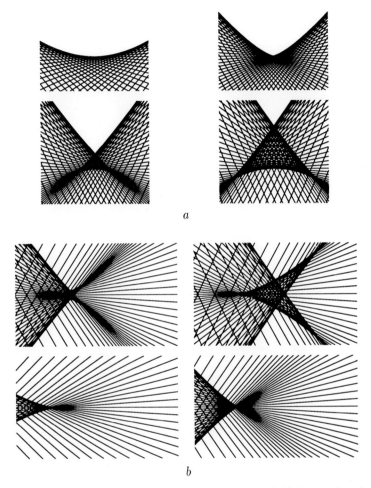

a

b

Figure 21   *Elementary catastrophes: a) Swallow-tail; b) Butterfly; c) Cusp;
d) Elliptic umbilics.*

2. Cusp (A_3):

$$(1/4)x^4 + (a/2)x^2 + bx \ . \tag{2.32}$$

Critical points of this catastrophe are determined by the equation

$$V'(x, a, b) = x^3 + ax + b = 0 \ .$$

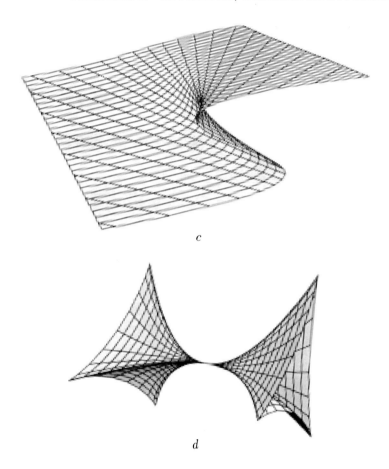

c

d

The separatrix

$$4a^3 + 27b^2 = 0$$

divides the space of control parameters into two regions.

Catastrophe of type A_{-3} having the form

$$- (1/4)x^4 - (a/2)x^2 - bx \qquad (2.33)$$

is the double cusp.

In going from the cusp to the double cusp, the maximum and minimum change places. Physically this leads to quite different results, since the cusp in contrast with the double cusp always possesses at least one global minimum.

3. Swallowtail (A_4):

$$(1/5)x^5 + (a/3)x^3 + (b/2)x^2 + cx .\qquad(2.34)$$

4. Elliptic umbilics (D_{+4}):

$$x^2y + y^3 + ay^2 + by + cx .\qquad(2.35)$$

5. Hyperbolic umbilics (D_{-4}):

$$x^2y - y^3 + ay^2 + by + cx .\qquad(2.36)$$

These singularities are structurally stable.

The power of catastrophe theory lies in the possibility of obtaining qualitative properties of physical systems as a function of n and k. In other words, for a given number of control parameters one can obtain the behavior of typical functions, while the shape of the catastrophe can define the number of those parameters (Figure 22).

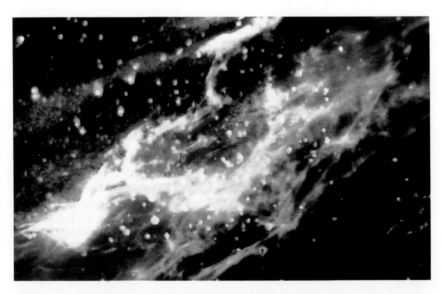

Figure 22 *Elementary catastrophes in the Universe: caustics of the Cygnus loop supernova remnant (from J. Graham, Sky and Telescope, July, 1991).*

Bibliography

A survey of differential geometry is contained in:

[1] Kobayashi S. and Nomizu K., *Foundations of Differential Geometry*, John Wiley, New York, 1963;

A presentation for physicists is given in:

[2] Hawking S.W. and Ellis G.F.R., *The Large-Scale Structure of Space-Time*, Cambridge University Press, 1973.

Essential properties of dynamical systems are covered in the classic book:

[3] Arnold V.I., *Mathematical Methods of Classical Mechanics*, Springer-Verlag, 1989.

For the basics of the ergodic theory see:

[4] Sinai Ya.G., *Introduction to Ergodic Theory*, Yerevan University Press, Yerevan, 1973; English transl.: *Math. Notes*, **18**, Princeton University Press, 1976.

[5] Cornfeld I.P., Fomin S.V. and Sinai Ya.G., *Ergodic Theory*, Springer-Verlag, 1982.

[6] Martin N.F.G. and England J.W., *Mathematical Theory of Entropy*, Addison-Wesley Publ., 1981.

Applications of ergodic theory to astrophysical problems can be found in:

[7] Gurzadyan V.G., Pfenniger D. (Eds.), *Ergodic Concepts in Stellar Dynamics*, Lecture Notes in Physics, Springer-Verlag, 1994.

The KS-entropy has been introduced in:

[8] Kolmogorov A.N., New Metric Invariants of the Transitive Dynamical Systems and Automorphisms of Lebesgue Spaces, *Doklady AN SSSR*, **119**, p.861, 1958.

The properties of time correlation functions are studied in:

[9] Ruelle D., *Thermodynamic Formalism*, Addison-Wesley, 1978;

and are applied to various physical systems in:

[10] Sagdeev R.Z., Usikov D.A. and Zaslavsky G.M., *Nonlinear Physics*, Harwood Academic Publishers, New York, 1988.

The methods of catastrophe theory are described in:

[11] Poston T. and Stewart N.I., *Catastrophe Theory and Applications*, London, Pitman, 1978.

[12] Arnold V.I., *Singularities of Caustics and Wave Fronts*, Kluwer Academic Publishers, 1990.

[13] Thom R., *Structural Stability and Morphogenesis*, Addison-Wesley Publ. Co., 1989.

Chapter 3

GALAXY CLUSTERS

The most analytically narrative and discredited academicism
can all become sublime hierarchies of thought
and the means of approach to new exactitudes of concrete irrationality.
Salvador Dali

3.1   The Cluster as a Basic Concept

The concept of a cluster of galaxies, if not the most basic concept, is certainly among one of the most basic ones in the study of the large-scale structure of the Universe. This can be most clearly seen if one tries to distinguish schematically the typical steps in the analysis of observational data. Initially, more straightforward methods such as galaxy counts and various statistical or smoothing tests are used to identify the voids, coherent matter structures, large-scale motions, etc. More refined examination of this data together with certain key assumptions is required to derive conclusions regarding the existence of a large amount of dark matter, the fractal nature of the matter distribution on galactic and cluster distance scales, etc. Finally, the information so obtained (or a considerable part of it) is used as a basis for numerous theories, models, or scenarios proposed to explain the origin and evolution of the observed filamentary structures. Among the reasons that many of these models are not very highly reliable is that observational "facts" are actually only tentative interpretations of the real situation, involving many disputable assumptions and an uncertainty in the understanding of key observational concepts and quantities.

However, a proper theoretical investigation of a physical problem should at least start with the definition of the basic concepts appropriate to its description. A good example of this is stellar dynamics, which due to the

49

efforts of Jeans, Schwarzschild, Eddington, Chandrasekhar, Ambartsumian, Spitzer and others can now be considered not only as belonging to astronomy but also to theoretical physics. In order to have such a correctly formulated problem of the large-scale structure of the Universe, one should have a rigorous description of a cluster of galaxies. Rubin in her concluding remarks at the 1987 Vatican Study Week compared the desired situation with that of the well established concept of a galaxy.

Our aim is thus to obtain a mathematically rigorous description of the concept of a cluster of galaxies which reflects its key properties. As an early attempt at such a definition one can recall the concept of Trapezium-type galaxy configurations introduced by Ambartsumian in his 1958 Solvay report. The problem in its general formulation, however, is more complicated and in fact should include the description of the hierarchy of subsystems of a given system. The background for our approach is the theory of dynamical systems, including some of the methods described in Chapter 2.

An essential advantage of our analysis is the possibility to describe simultaneously the concepts of groups of galaxies and rich or poor clusters, etc., by varying a certain numerical quantity. This method is not only adequate to accomplish the goal of our investigation, namely to decipher the substructure of the observed filaments, but also has a number of other applications, particularly in the evolution of galactic systems. This approach can be more useful if combined with those for the smoothing of peculiar velocity fields and the reconstruction methods for the 3-velocity and the mass density distribution.

3.2   Clusters Defined by Dynamical Systems

Our first goal therefore is to split a system of objects into subsystems which have the same properties. We will consider a subsystem of a given system to be a subset of objects whose internal connection is stronger than that of external ones be some criterion. We now try to make this idea more precise.

Suppose the set $\mathcal{A}$ is split into a finite set of pairwise disjoint subsets $\{\mathcal{A}_i\}$ whose union is $\mathcal{A}$ itself, i.e., $\{\mathcal{A}_i\}$ is a partition of the set $\mathcal{A}$ as described for manifolds in Chapter 2, now convenient to call a splitting of $\mathcal{A}$

1. $\mathcal{A} = \bigcup_{k=1}^{d} \mathcal{A}_k,$

2. $\forall i, j \in \{1, \ldots, d\},\ i \neq j,\ \mathcal{A}_i \cap \mathcal{A}_j = \emptyset$.

The number of subsets d is called the degree of the splitting.

Let $\mathcal{A}$ be a set, $\mathcal{B}(\mathcal{A})$ the set of all subsets of $\mathcal{A}$, and let $\mathcal{S}$ be the set of all pairs $(\mathcal{X}, \mathcal{Y})$ of such subsets for which $\mathcal{Y}$ is contained in $\mathcal{X}$

$$\mathcal{S}(\mathcal{A}) \equiv \bigcup_{\mathcal{X} \in \mathcal{B}(\mathcal{A})} \bigcup_{\mathcal{Y} \in \mathcal{B}(\mathcal{X})} (\mathcal{X}, \mathcal{Y}) \subset \mathcal{B}(\mathcal{A}) \times \mathcal{B}(\mathcal{A}) \ .$$

Suppose one can introduce some non-negative function $\mathcal{P}$ called the boundness function which describes the degree of interaction of $\mathcal{Y}$ with the complimentary set $\mathcal{X} \backslash \mathcal{Y}$ within $\mathcal{X}$ according to some criterion. The following notation is convenient

$$\mathcal{P} : \mathcal{S}(\mathcal{A}) \to R_+ : (\mathcal{X}, \mathcal{Y}) \mapsto \mathcal{P}_\mathcal{X}(\mathcal{Y}), \tag{3.1}$$

where R_+ is the set of nonnegative real numbers. Using such a boundness function the "error" of a splitting of $\mathcal{A}$ can be measured by a non-negative real number ρ (small ρ means small "error") in the following way.

A subset $\mathcal{A}_k$ from this splitting is called ρ-free in $\mathcal{A}$ if the maximum value of the boundness function $\mathcal{P}_\mathcal{A}(\cdot)$ associated with the whole set when evaluated on this subset and its compliment is less than or equal to ρ

$$\mathcal{A}_k \ \rho\text{-free in } \mathcal{A} \iff \max\{\mathcal{P}_\mathcal{A}(\mathcal{A}_k), \mathcal{P}_\mathcal{A}(\mathcal{A} \backslash \mathcal{A}_k)\} \le \rho \ .$$

A subset $\mathcal{A}_k$ is called a ρ-subsystem if it is ρ-free in $\mathcal{A}$ and if it contains no subset B which is ρ-free in $\mathcal{A}_k$ (excluding the empty set and itself)

$$\forall B \in \mathcal{B}(\mathcal{A}_k) \backslash (\mathcal{A}_k \bigcup \{\emptyset\}) \ , \qquad \max\{\mathcal{P}_{\mathcal{A}_k}(B), \mathcal{P}_{\mathcal{A}_k}(\mathcal{A}_k \backslash B)\} > \rho \ .$$

We are then led to the following definition.

Definition. A splitting $\{\mathcal{A}_1, \ldots, \mathcal{A}_d\}$ of $\mathcal{A}$ into ρ-subsystems $\mathcal{A}_k$, $k \in \{1, \ldots, d\}$ is called a ρ-partition of the pair $(\mathcal{A}, \mathcal{P})$, i.e., of $\mathcal{A}$ with respect to the boundness function $\mathcal{P}$.

The subsets $\mathcal{A}_k$ will be referred to as ρ-subsystems of $\mathcal{A}$.

Denote by $\Sigma(\rho)$ the set of all possible ρ-partitions $\{\mathcal{A}_1, \ldots, \mathcal{A}_d\}$ of $(\mathcal{A}, \mathcal{P})$. Our goal is to obtain the multifunction Σ:

$$\Sigma : R_+ \to \{\rho\text{-partitions}\} : \rho \mapsto \Sigma(\rho) \ . \tag{3.2}$$

3.3   S-Tree

To introduce the concept of a cluster let us start with the simplest system of point particles interacting according to a given force law in R^3. We wish to describe the degree of boundness of those particles in various ways.

To accomplish this goal we propose the following natural approach. Let $x_1(t)$ and $x_2(t)$, $t \in (-T, T)$ be the trajectories of the two particles when the interaction is taken into account, and let $y_1(t)$ and $y_2(t)$ be the corresponding trajectories when the interaction is "switched off", related to the former trajectories by sharing the same initial data at time zero as the corresponding interacting particles. In other words $y_1(t)$ and $y_2(t)$ are the trajectories of free particles for which $y_i(0) = x_i(0)$, $\dot{y}_i(0) = \dot{x}_i(0)$, $i = 1, 2$.

Let us measure the degree of boundness of the two interacting particles over this time period by the function

$$m = \max_{i=1,2} \mathcal{N}(x_i(\cdot) - y_i(\cdot)), \qquad (3.3)$$

i.e., the maximum "deviation" of either of the trajectories of the interacting particles from its corresponding free trajectories, where this deviation is measured with respect to the following local norm $\mathcal{N}$ on C^∞ parametrized curves in R^3 over the interval $(-T, T)$

$$\mathcal{N}(z(\cdot)) = \sup_{t \in (-T, T)} \{|z(t)|, |\dot{z}(t)|\}. \qquad (3.4)$$

Now consider the following balls of radius r at each trajectories $y_i(\cdot)$ of the two free particles

$$\mathcal{C}_i(r) = \{z(\cdot) | \mathcal{N}(z(\cdot) - y_i(\cdot)) \leq r\}, \; i = 1, 2 \;.$$

m is the minimal allowed radius such that neither of the interacting particle trajectories escapes from its corresponding free-zone-space $\mathcal{C}_i(m)$. Therefore two particles are considered to be ρ-free for $\rho > 0$ if $m \leq \rho$ (Figure 23).

We now give a more precise formulation of these ideas. Consider a dynamical system characterized by the following equations:

$$\ddot{x}_a = f_a(x), \; x \in R^{dN}, \; x_a \in R^d \;.$$

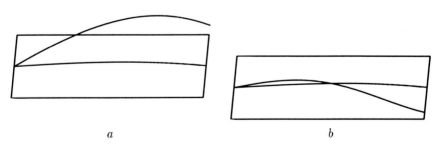

a   b

Figure 23 *Bound (a) and free (b) particles.*

For the problem of interest the smooth functions f_a have the binary form

$$f_a(x) = \sum_{b=1}^{N} f_{ab}(x_a, x_b) ,$$

where $f_{aa}(x_a, x_a)$ indicates the influence of an external field on the a-th particle.

We now define the boundness function $\mathcal{P}_{\mathcal{Z}}(\mathcal{Y})$, where $\mathcal{Y} \subset \mathcal{Z} \subset \mathcal{A}$. Consider the following two systems:

Z.

$$\ddot{z}_a = \sum_{b \in \mathcal{Z}} f_{ab}(z_a, z_b),$$

$$z_a(0) = c_a, \ \dot{z}_a(0) = v_a, \ \text{where } a \in \mathcal{Z} ,$$

Y.

$$\ddot{y}_a = \sum_{b \in \mathcal{Y}} f_{ab}(y_a, y_b) ,$$

$$y_a(0) = c_a, \ \dot{y}_a(0) = v_a, \ \text{where } a \in \mathcal{Y} ,$$

where c_a and v_a are constant vectors. the initial position and velocity, respectively, of the a-th particle. The first dynamical system represents the subsystem of particles in $\mathcal{Z}$ switching off the interactions with external particles in $\mathcal{A} \backslash \mathcal{Z}$, while the second is the same for particles in $\mathcal{Y}$.

Then for the given local norm $\mathcal{N}$ we take

$$\mathcal{P}_{\mathcal{Z}}(\mathcal{Y}) = \max_{a \in \mathcal{Y}} \mathcal{N}(z_a(\cdot) - y_a(\cdot)), \tag{3.5}$$

where $z_a(t), y_a(t)$ are the solutions of the systems of equations **Z** and **Y** respectively for some time interval $(-T, T)$. In other words the boundness of $\mathcal{Y}$ in $\mathcal{Z}$ is the maximum deviation of the trajectories of its particles taking into account only internal interactions compared to the situation when interactions with particles in $\mathcal{Z}$ are also included. Our goal is to split $\mathcal{A}$ into ρ-subsystems according to the our definition, i.e., to obtain the map Σ for this choice of boundness function.

Problem 1. Obtain the ρ-partitions of the given pair $(\mathcal{A}, \mathcal{P})$. Thus for given value of ρ we obtain a partition $\Sigma(\rho)$ of the set $\mathcal{A}$, i.e. obtain the multifunction Σ

$$\Sigma : R_+ \to \mathcal{B}(\mathcal{B}(N)) . \tag{3.6}$$

It is easy to see that the set $\mathcal{A}(\rho) \in \Sigma(\rho)$ containing the a-th particle cannot be enlarged by increasing ρ, i.e., if there exists an a such that

$$a \in \mathcal{A}(\rho) \in \Sigma(\rho), \qquad a \in \mathcal{B}(\rho) \in \Sigma(\rho) \ ,$$

then

$$\rho_1 < \rho_2 \Rightarrow \mathcal{A}(\rho_1) \supset \mathcal{B}(\rho_2) \ .$$

Therefore one can represent this multifunction by means of a tree-graph (Figure 24). We will say that ρ_* is a bifurcation point of Σ if

$$\forall \varepsilon_1 \in (0, \rho_*), \ \forall \varepsilon_2 > 0 \quad \Sigma(\rho_* - \varepsilon_1) \neq \Sigma(\rho_* + \varepsilon_2).$$

Clearly the number of these bifurcation points is finite, $\Sigma(\cdot)$ being constant between each subsequent bifurcation points, and there exist ρ_{min} and ρ_{max} such that:

$$\Sigma(\rho) = \quad \{\{1, \ldots, N\}\}, \quad \rho < \rho_{min} \ ,$$
$$\Sigma(\rho) = \quad \{\{1\}, \ldots, \{N\}\}, \quad \rho > \rho_{max} \ .$$

If the "error" of a splitting is small enough $\rho < \rho_{min}$, then the partition (first one) is the partition with minimal degree of splitting $d = 1$ and subsystem $\mathcal{A}_1 = \mathcal{A} = \{1, \ldots, N\}$. The latter partition has the maximal degree $d = N$ and $\mathcal{A}_k = \{k\}$. That is to say, each particle of the system is a subsystem, i.e. every particle is ρ-free if $\rho > \rho_{max}$.

Finally let us now introduce equivalence classes for multifunctions. Two multifunctions Σ_1, Σ_2 will be considered to be equivalent $\Sigma_1 \sim \Sigma_2$ if $\exists \phi$:

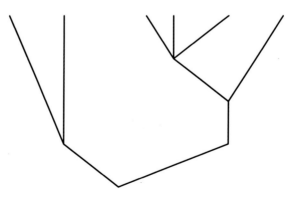

Figure 24 *Multifunction Σ as a tree-graph.*

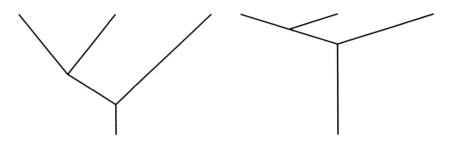

Figure 25 *Equivalent trees.*

$R_+ \rightarrow R_+$ smooth monotonous function (i.e., $\rho_1 < \rho_2 \Rightarrow \phi(\rho_1) < \phi(\rho_2)$), such that (Figure 25)

$$\forall \rho \in R_+, \qquad \Sigma_1(\phi(\rho)) = \Sigma_2(\rho) \ .$$

Definition. We call an equivalence class a Subsystem-Tree or simply an S-Tree.

Problem 2 (Main problem). Obtain the S-Tree for a given $(\mathcal{A}, \mathcal{P})$.

Bibliography

The approach described in this section was introduced in:

[1] Gurzadyan V.G., Harutyunyan V.V., and Kocharyan A.A., Large-Scale Structure of the Universe: Mathematical Formulation of the Problem, in: *Proc. II DAEC Meeting "The Distribution of Matter in the Universe* Eds. G. Mamon, D. Gerbal, Editions Observatoire de Paris, 1991, p.333.

[2] Gurzadyan V.G., Harutyunyan V.V., and Kocharyan A.A., A Method for Defining Structures in the Distribution of Galaxies, *Astr. Ap.*, **281**, p.964. 1994.

For the smoothing of the large-scale velocity field based on the potential flow ansatz see:

[3] Dekel A., Reconstruction Methods in Cosmology, in: *Physical Cosmology*, Eds. A. Blanchard, L. Cernikier, M. Lachieze-Rey, and J. Tran Thanh Van, Editions Frontieres, 1991.

Chapter 4

THE S-TREE TECHNIQUE

We are moving towards serenity by
simplification of ideas and means.
Henri Matisse

The definition of a cluster given in the previous chapter can be used in a computer analysis of the substructure of a given galactic system, including the search for and identification of bound groups and clusters of galaxies as well as unbound (field) galaxies, and the analysis of large-scale motions, etc. In this chapter we present an example of a special numerical algorithm which accomplishes this goal. The "S-tree" technique which solves the problem is then applied to decipher the substructure of two actual galactic systems, the Local Group and the cluster Abell 754. This technique can be especially useful in the investigation of the evolution of clusters of galaxies, as well as in studying the problem of dark matter.

4.1   The Measure of Influence

Suppose the system under study consist of N elements, labeled by the integers $\mathcal{A} = \{1, \ldots, N\}$ as in the previous chapter. The description of the algorithm begins with the introduction of a positive entry matrix D_{ab} $a, b \in \mathcal{A}$, which describes in some way the degree of boundness of a pair of elements with labels a and b. The specific choice of the matrix D depends on the physical system and its properties. We are of course interested in systems interacting via Newtonian gravity.

Once this choice is made, one can then introduce a corresponding 1-parameter family of matrices $\Gamma_{ab}(\rho)$ of zero or unit entries assigned by comparing the degree of boundness of each pair to a cutoff value (the parameter ρ)

$$\Gamma_{ab}(\rho) = \begin{cases} 0 & \text{if } D_{ab} \le \rho \text{ and } D_{ba} \le \rho , \\ 1 & \text{if } D_{ab} > \rho \text{ or } D_{ba} > \rho . \end{cases} \qquad (4.1)$$

The matrix $\Gamma(\rho)$ can be used to associate a graph with N vertices to the set $\mathcal{A}$, with the vertices corresponding to a pair a and b being connected by a line if $\Gamma_{ab}(\rho) = 1$. Similarly one can associate a subgraph with any subset $A \subset \mathcal{A}$ of k elements; such a subgraph is said to be connected if every pair of vertices in it is connected by some unbroken sequence of connected vertices.

The definition of a ρ-subsystem cluster given in section 3.3 can now be reformulated as a subset of particles with labels A which correspond to a connected subgraph of the graph associated with $\Gamma(\rho)$ such that there is no other subset $B \supset A$ containing A which has a connected subgraph associated with it. (In other words no other vertex of the total graph is connected to the subgraph.)

If one defines the boundness function $\mathcal{P}$ of section 3.3 by

$$\mathcal{P}_X(Y) = \max_{\substack{y \in Y \\ z \in X \backslash Y}} \{ D_{yz} \} , \qquad (4.2)$$

the problem searching for a ρ-subsystem cluster is then reduced to looking for a connected subgraph of the one associated with $\Gamma(\rho)$ (Figure 26).

It is readily seen that

$$
\begin{aligned}
\max\{\mathcal{P}_X(Y), \mathcal{P}_X(Y\backslash X)\} \;&=\; \max\{ \max_{\substack{y \in Y \\ z \in X \backslash Y}} \{D_{yz}\}, \max_{\substack{y \in X \backslash Y \\ z \in Y}} \{D_{yz}\} \} \\
&=\; \max\{ \max_{\substack{y \in Y \\ z \in X \backslash Y}} \{D_{yz}\}, \max_{\substack{y \in Y \\ z \in X \backslash Y}} \{D_{zy}\} \} \\
&=\; \max_{\substack{y \in Y \\ z \in X \backslash Y}} \{D_{yz}, D_{zy}\},
\end{aligned}
$$

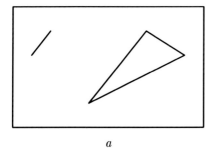
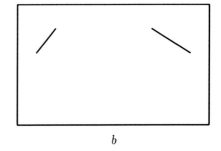

a b

Figure 26 *Subclustering when a)* $D_{35} = D_{53} > \rho > D_{23} = D_{32}$ *and b)* $\rho > D_{35} = D_{53}$. *In this figure D is the inverse distance.*

therefore

$$\max\{\mathcal{P}_X(Y), \mathcal{P}_X(Y/X)\} \le \rho$$

if and only if

$$\max_{\substack{y \in Y \\ z \in X \backslash Y}} \{D_{yz}, D_{zy}\} \le \rho ,$$

hence Y is ρ-free in X if for any $y \in Y$ and $z \in X \backslash Y$ the following conditions hold

$$D_{yz} \le \rho \text{ and } D_{zy} \le \rho,$$

but these are nothing but the following: for any $y \in Y$ and $z \in X \backslash Y$

$$\Gamma_{yz}(\rho) = \Gamma_{zy}(\rho) = 0.$$

So Y is ρ-free in X if the corresponding vertices to the set Y are a subgraph of the graph X with the matrix $\Gamma(\rho)$. Similarly one can show that Y is a ρ-subsystem if it is a connected subgraph in X.

Consider now how the matrix D can be chosen if $d = 3$ and the equations of motion are those of Newtonian gravity

$$M_a \ddot{x}_a^i = \sum_{b \in A \backslash \{a\}} f_{ab}^i,$$

$$f_{ab} = -GM_aM_b \frac{x_a - x_b}{|x_a - x_b|^3}, \quad a \ne b, \tag{4.3}$$

$$f_{aa} = 0,$$

where M_a is the mass of a-th particle and

$$|x_a| = \left(\sum_{i=1}^{3} \left[x_a^i \right]^2 \right)^{1/2} .$$

We propose the following possible choices for the matrix D which will be categorized by obvious labels; the first two involve only properties of a pair of particles at a given instant

a) Distance:

$$D_{ab} = |x_a - x_b|^{-1} . \tag{4.4}$$

This choice implies that two particles are more strongly bound when they are closer together. This is a pure positional description and does not take into account the particle masses nor any dynamical information, i.e., the velocities. It is similar to the visual statistical methods described in Chapter 6.

b) Force:

$$D_{ab} = |f_{ab}| \tag{4.5}$$

In this case a stronger force of interaction means a stronger binding between the particles. The masses are now taken into account, but the description is again a local or pointwise one.

Next we discuss a class of choices for D which are related to the perturbation of the system. The choice should reflect the degree of deviation of the a-th particle from its "natural" trajectory when the position of the b-th one is disturbed. More precisely, if the trajectory of the b-th particle $x_b(\cdot)$ is disturbed at some initial moment, then the trajectory $x_a(\cdot)$ of the a-th one should be

$$\tilde{x}_a(\cdot) = x_a(\cdot) + \delta x_a(\cdot) \ ,$$

where

$$\delta x_a(0) = \begin{cases} \delta_0 & a = b \\ 0 & a \neq b \ . \end{cases}$$

Here $\delta x_a(\cdot)$ describes the influence of the perturbation on the trajectory and can be used to measure the stability of the trajectory. The following choices of the matrix D use this information

c) Potential:

$$D_{ab} = \max_{i,j} \left\{ -\frac{\partial^2 V_{ab}}{\partial x_a^i \partial x_b^j}, 0 \right\} = \max_{i,j} \left\{ \frac{\partial f_{ab}^i}{\partial x_b^j}, 0 \right\} \ , \tag{4.6}$$

where

$$V_{ab} = \frac{G M_a M_b}{|x_a - x_b|}.$$

Since

$$M_a \ddot{x}_a^i = \sum_{b \in \mathcal{A} \backslash \{a\}} f_{ab}^i,$$

$$M_a \delta \ddot{x}_a^i = \sum_{b \in \mathcal{A} \backslash \{a\}} \sum_{j=1}^{3} \frac{\partial f_{ab}^i}{\partial x_b^j} \delta x_b^j \ ,$$

two particles are more strongly bound the bigger the influence of one's perturbation on the other is.

However, the dynamics of the system is still not taken into account. The following two quantities avoid this drawback by including the dynamical information as well. They both rely on the Maupertuis principle reformulation of the dynamics.

As shown in Chapter 2, the Maupertuis principle allows one to represent a Hamiltonian flow as a geodesic flow in a $3N$-dimensional Riemannian manifold with a certain metric. The stability properties of the Hamiltonian system may then be studied using the geodesic deviation equation. The configuration space for the N-particle system presently being considered has the $3N$ coordinates $\{x^\mu\} = \{x_a^i\}$, using a single index μ to represent the pair (a, i) of particle and Cartesian coordinate labels. The natural metric g associated with the kinetic energy function has the coordinate components $g_{\mu\nu} = M_a \delta_{\mu\nu}$. To express the geodesic equation, some notation is useful. First let

$$R_{ab}^i = x_a^i - x_b^i , \qquad R_{ab} = |R_{ab}^i|$$

abbreviate the interparticle separation vector and its magnitude.

Expressing the kinetic energy function W in terms of the total energy and the potential energy for the system one has

$$W = E + \sum_{a=1}^{N} \sum_{b=1}^{a-1} G \frac{M_a M_b}{R_{ab}} . \tag{4.7}$$

The rescaled metric of the equivalent geodesic flow is then

$$G_{\mu\nu} = W g_{\mu\nu} , \tag{4.8}$$

leading to the unit tangent vector

$$u^\mu = u^{(a,i)} = \frac{\dot{x}_a^i}{\sqrt{2W}} \tag{4.9}$$

with respect to this latter metric. However, it is convenient to allow its indices to be shifted with the original simpler metric, defining the quantities

$$u_\mu = g_{\mu\nu} u^\nu , \qquad \|u\|^2 = u^\nu u_\nu = 1/W ,$$

where the last equality is valid only after using the energy constraint to replace the kinetic energy function by W. The coordinate derivatives of the components of G lead to derivatives of the function W on the configuration space, for which a subscript notation is used; the indices so generated are also shifted with the original metric. The first and second derivatives are explicitly

$$W_\mu = W_{(a,i)} = -\sum_{\substack{c=1 \\ c \neq a}}^{N} G \frac{M_a M_c R_{ac}^i}{R_{ac}^3} ,$$

$$W_{\mu\nu} = W_{(a,i)(b,j)} = \begin{cases} G \frac{M_a M_b}{R_{ab}^3} \left(\delta_{ij} - \frac{3 R_{ab}^i R_{ab}^j}{R_{ab}^2} \right) & \text{if } a \neq b , \\ -\sum_{\substack{c=1 \\ c \neq a}}^{N} G \frac{M_a M_c}{R_{ac}^3} \left(\delta_{ij} - \frac{3 R_{ac}^i R_{ac}^j}{R_{ac}^2} \right) & \text{if } a = b . \end{cases}$$

The following quantities are also useful

$$\|dW\|^2 = \sum_{a=1}^{N}\sum_{i=1}^{3} W_{(a,i)}^2/M_a \ ,$$

$$W_\mu u^\mu = \sum_{a=1}^{N}\sum_{i=1}^{3} W_{(a,i)} u^{(a,i)} \ ,$$

$$W_{\mu\nu} u^\mu u^\nu = \sum_{a=1}^{N}\sum_{i=1}^{3}\sum_{b=1}^{N}\sum_{j=1}^{3} W_{(a,i)(b,j)} u^{(a,i)} u^{(b,j)} \ ,$$

$$W_{\mu\nu} u^\nu = \sum_{b=1}^{N}\sum_{j=1}^{3} W_{(a,i)(b,j)} u^{(b,j)} \ .$$

In terms of these quantities, the tensor K (2.9) of the Jacobi equation (2.8)

$$\ddot{n}^\mu + K^\mu{}_\nu n^\nu = 0$$

has the expression

$$K^\mu{}_\nu = -\frac{1}{2W}\left[\delta^\mu{}_\nu W_{\lambda\rho}u^\lambda u^\rho + W^\mu{}_\nu\|u\|^2 - u^\mu W_{\lambda\nu}u^\lambda - u_\nu W^\mu{}_\lambda u^\lambda\right]$$

$$-\frac{3}{4W^2}\left[\left(u^\mu W_\nu - \delta^\mu{}_\nu W_\lambda u^\lambda\right)W_\rho u^\rho + \left(u_\nu W_\lambda u^\lambda - W_\nu\|u\|^2\right)W^\mu\right]$$

$$-\frac{1}{4W^2}\left[\delta^\mu{}_\nu\|u\|^2 - u^\mu u_\nu\right]\|dW\|^2 \ .$$

$$(4.10)$$

Given this background, two further choices of the matrix D may be introduced.

f) N-Curvature:

$$D_{ab} = \max_{i,j}\left\{-K^\mu{}_\nu, 0\right\} \ ,   (4.11)$$

where $\mu = (a,i)$, $\nu = (b,j)$. So the a-th and b-th particles are more strongly bound the bigger the maximum with respect to the space coordinates (i and j) of the influence of the perturbation. According to the Jacobi equation the latter is determined by the Riemann tensor of the metric (4.8) along $\mathbf{u}$ (velocities of each of the particles (4.9)), i.e., determined by $K^\mu{}_\nu$ (4.10) where W is defined as in (4.7). Therefore the dynamics of the system is taken into account in an essential way.

g) 2-Curvature:

$$D_{ab} = \max_{i,j}\left\{-k^\mu{}_\nu, 0\right\},   (4.12)$$

where k is the same curvature for the 2-particle system ignoring all particles except the pair a and b. That is to say

$$W = E + G\frac{M_a M_b}{R_{ab}} \, ,$$

and $k^\mu{}_\nu$ is expressed via the same equation (4.10) as for the previous case.

4.2 Computer Analysis Strategy

Next we discuss both the operational procedure for implementing these ideas as an algorithm to analyze the substructure of the N-particle self-gravitating system and also the ways in which the results may be presented. For a given choice of the matrix D which measures the boundness of the particle pairs, the first step is to evaluate the multifunction Σ which identifies the bound subsystems for a given value ρ of its argument. As shown above, for given D and ρ the problem is reduced to the search for the connected parts of the graph associated with the matrix $\Gamma(\rho)$.

First, $\mathcal{P}$ is obtained for all values of ρ in the following way. The equations of motion of a gravitating system are solved by the Runge-Kutta method and the corresponding trajectories $z_a(t)$, the solution of system $\mathbf{Z}$, are compared to $y_a(t)$, the solution of the system $\mathbf{Y}$, using the local norm $\mathcal{N}$. Then having obtained all $\mathcal{P}_Z Y$, one has the multifunction Σ.

Thus we use an algorithm which obtains all connected parts of the graph Γ for all values of ρ. In other words, given the parameters

$$M_a, \ x_a(0), \ \dot{x}_a(0), \ a \in \mathcal{A}$$

and the matrix D, the algorithm produces the function Σ. The latter can be represented in the form of tree-graph as follows.

Assume that multifunction Σ has m bifurcation points

$$0 = \rho_0 < \rho_1 < \ldots < \rho_m < \infty \, .$$

Let

$$\Sigma_k = \Sigma(\rho_k) = \{\mathcal{A}_1^k, \ldots, \mathcal{A}_{d_k}^k\} \qquad 0 \le k \le m \, .$$

The tree-graph corresponding to the multifunction Σ is defined to be a graph with $\{\mathcal{A}_i^k\}$ apexes, where $0 \le k \le m$ and i runs over $1, \ldots, d_k$ for any k, associated with the matrix T.

$$T(\mathcal{A}_i^k, \mathcal{A}_j^h) = \begin{cases} 1 & \text{if } k = h+1 \text{ and } \mathcal{A}_i^k \subset \mathcal{A}_j^h \, , \\ 1 & \text{if } h = k+1 \text{ and } \mathcal{A}_j^h \subset \mathcal{A}_i^k \, , \\ 0 & \text{otherwise} \, . \end{cases}$$

For example, if $N = 4$ the tree-graph of the multifunction Σ

$$\Sigma(\rho) = \begin{cases} \Sigma_0 = \{\{1,2,3,4\}\} & d_0 = 1 \quad 0 \leq \rho < 2 = \rho_1 \\ \Sigma_1 = \{\{1,2\},\{3,4\}\} & d_1 = 2 \quad 2 \leq \rho < 4 = \rho_2 \\ \Sigma_2 = \{\{1,2\},\{3\},\{4\}\} & d_2 = 3 \quad 4 \leq \rho < 7 = \rho_3 \\ \Sigma_3 = \{\{1\},\{2\},\{3\},\{4\}\} & d_3 = 4 \quad 7 \leq \rho < \infty \end{cases}$$

has the form as shown in Figure 24. Here d denotes the number of cluster-subsystems, e.g., for $\rho = 1$ all four particles form a single ($d_0 = 1$) cluster $\mathcal{A}_1^0(1) = \{1,2,3,4\}$; for $\rho = 5$ there are $d_2 = 3$ clusters, one containing two particles $\{1,2\}$ and two others have one particle each.

However, such a figure is most convenient for systems with not too large a value of $N, (N \simeq 10)$ as shown in Figure 27. For larger values of N one can use N-particle graphics with separated groups distinguished by different colors. The function Σ and corresponding tree-graph can then represented

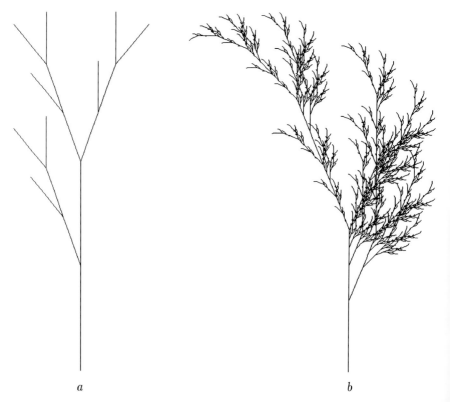

a b

Figure 27 *Trees for small and big N.*

by a "movie" $(\Sigma_0, \Sigma_1, \ldots, \Sigma_m)$ with ρ playing the role of the time elapsing in the movie. As ρ changes, the modification in the substructure can be seen.

4.3 Substructure of Real Filaments:
I. Local Group, II. Abell 754

We now apply the method just described to study the dynamical structure of two actual systems of galaxies which are of particular interest. The object of doing this is to illustrate the possibilities of the method rather than discuss the astrophysical consequences of the results of the calculations; the latter can be found in original papers listed in the Bibliography along with the sources of observational data. For both systems the matrix

$$D_{ab} = \max_{i,j}\{-k^\mu \nu, 0\}, \tag{4.13}$$

has been used during computer simulations.

I. Local Group of Galaxies. The Local Group is one of the best studied clusters of galaxies. From this reason the study of the Local Group with an alternative technique also provides a unique opportunity to compare its results with those of the others.

As emphasized earlier, the key point of the tree-diagram technique is the simultaneous use of both spatial and dynamical information about the system. Namely, the required data in addition to the galactic 3-coordinates include peculiar velocities and relative masses or luminosities, i.e., absolute magnitudes when the mass to luminosity ratio M/L can be considered constant. The latter assumption has been used in the present calculations and is evidently subject to improvement along with other observational data presented in Table 1.

The results of our analysis of the sample of galaxies considered to be members of the Local Group are in general agreement with those performed by other methods. The present study establishes the existence of a single physical system, i.e., members of which mutually influence each other. This system contains both giant spirals, the Milky Way Galaxy and $M31$, Andromeda galaxy, and other galaxies associated with them. Several galaxies assumed by some authors to be possible members of the Local Group and therefore also listed in Table 1 are actually shown not to be influenced by the Group or by each other. The Local Group defined by this interacting system only according to observational data extends less than $2Mpc$.

Increasing the degree of boundness and thus exploring further subclustering clearly reveals two subsystems, one influenced by the Milky Way and the other by $M31$ as shown. Members of these two subsystems are listed in

Table 2 ordered by a decreasing degree of boundness to the Milky Way and
M31, respectively.

Table 2.

Milky Way Subsystem		M31 Subsystem	
LMC, SMC		M32	
Sculptor S		NGC205	
Carina, Draco		NGC147	dE3
Fornax D		NGC185	dE5
Leo II	dEO pec	LGS 3	
Leo I	dE3	M33	
NGC6822	Im		
IC1613	Im		

Further increasing the boundness parameter indicates the pairs of galaxies, which are gravitationally influenced by each other stronger than by any
other object (or objects); note the similarity of morphological type within
each pair (Figure 28). Several galaxies are actually shown not to be influenced, thus being either field galaxies or members of other groups or clusters.
Listed below by increasing degree of boundness to the Milky Way-M31 system, they are as follows:

Table 3.

Maffei 2
U6456
NGC300
Sex B
NGC7793, IC4182
Maffei 1

Due to the possibility of obtaining the relative degrees of influence between galaxies, we see that, say Fornax D is less influenced by the Milky
Way than Carina or Draco, but more than NGC6822 and IC1613. Leo II
and Leo I are both influenced by it, but are much more bound to each other.

Abell 754.

The interest in this cluster is particularly connected with the controver-
sial results on the existence or absence of its subgroups as derived in various
studies. The results of the analysis by means of the tree-diagram technique
based on the data on the peculiar velocities of 81 galaxies reveal the existence of subsystems of Abell 754 as exhibited in Figure 29. Several galaxies
which are shown not to have any correlation with the remaining ones appear
to be projected objects.

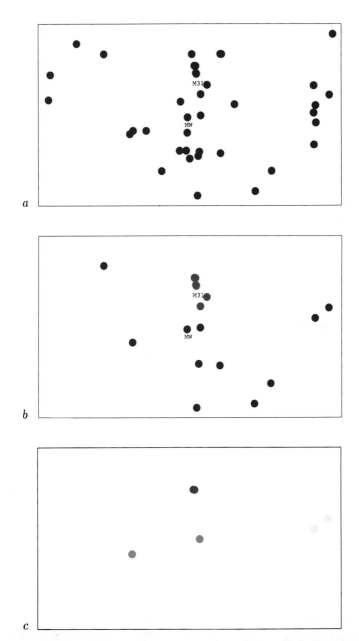

Figure 28 *Subclustering in the Local Group according to the S-tree method: the Milky Way and M31 subgroups as well as other strongly bound galaxies are shown.*

Figure 29 *The revealed substructure of the cluster of galaxies Abell 754.*

c

Figure 29 *(Continued)*

Bibliography

The technique described here is developed in:

[1] Gurzadyan V.G., Harutyunyan V.V., and Kocharyan A.A., Large-Scale Structure of the Universe: Mathematical Formulation of the Problem, in: *Proc. II DAEC Meeting "The Distribution of Matter in the Universe"*, Eds.G. Mamon, D. Gerbal, p.333, Meudon, 1991.

[2] Gurzadyan V.G., Harutyunyan V.V., and Kocharyan A.A., A Method for Defining Structures in the Distribution of Galaxies, *Astr. Ap.*, **281**, p.964, 1994.

LOCAL GROUP OF GALAXIES

Object	M_B	α 1950	δ 1950	velocity km/s	distance Mpc
1)$MilkyWay$	-20.5	00 00.00	00 00.0	0	0.0
2)$N55$	-20.0	00 12.40	-39 28.0	97 ± 3	1.4
3)$IC10$	-16.5	00 17.69	59 00.9	-44 ± 2	1.25
4)$N147$	-14.4	00 30.46	48 13.8	136 ± 50	0.7
5)$N185$	-14.4	00 36.19	48 03.7	67 ± 22	0.72
6)$N205$	-15.6	00 37.64	41 24.9	49 ± 11	0.64
7)$M31$	-21.4	00 40.00	40 59.7	-10 ± 1	0.67
8)$M32$	-15.4	00 39.97	40 35.5	86 ± 6	0.66
9)SMC	-16.4	00 51.00	-73 06.0	-21 ± 5	0.063
10)$N300$	-18.6	00 52.52	-37 57.4	100.2 ± 2	2.67
11)$SculptorS$	-10.5	00 57.60	-33 58.0	74	0.085
12)$LGS-3$	-9.6	01 01.20	21 37.0	-100 ± 8	0.72
13)$IC1613$	-14.4	01 02.22	01 51.0	-153 ± 3	0.64
14)$M33$	-18.4	01 31.05	30 23.9	-39 ± 0.5	0.82
15)$Maffei1$	-20.4	02 32.60	59 26.0	223	2.1
16)$FornaxD$	-12.0	02 37.84	-34 44.4	-51	0.19
17)$Maffei2$	-20.1	02 38.14	59 23.4	208	3.0
18)$IC342$	-20.2	03 41.95	67 56.4	221	1.84
19)LMC	-18.1	05 24.00	-69 48.0	13	0.052
20)$Carina$	-7.2	06 40.40	-50 55.0	14	0.093
21)$LeoA$	-13.1	09 56.53	30 59.2	-17 ± 10	1.59
22)$SexB$	-15.5	09 57.39	05 34.3	156 ± 10	2.68
23)$N3109$	-17.2	10 00.80	-25 54.8	193	1.6
24)$LeoI$	-10.9	10 05.77	12 33.2	117	0.22
25)$SexA$	-15.1	10 08.57	-04 27.7	154 ± 5	1.3
26)$LeoII$	-9.5	11 10.83	22 26.1	15	0.22
27)$U6456$	-12.0	11 24.60	79 16.0	47 ± 70	1.9
28)$DDO155$	-10.7	12 56.20	14 29.2	183 ± 5	1.0
29)$IC4182$	-16.9	13 03.51	37 52.5	373 ± 5	4.4
30)UM	-8.2	15 08.20	67 18.0	-88	0.065
31)$Draco$	-7.5	17 19.40	57 58.0	-95	0.075
32)$Sagittarius$	-9.1	19 27.01	-17 47.0	10.9 ± 1.4	1.11
33)$N6822$	-14.8	19 42.12	-14 55.7	55 ± 5	0.62
34)$DDO210$	-10.9	20 44.13	-13 02.0	-13 ± 10	1.5
35)$IC5152$	-14.4	21 59.60	-51 32.0	78 ± 15	1.51
36)Hog	-10.4	23 23.80	-32 40.0	75 ± 5	1.3
37)$Pegasus$	-13.4	23 26.05	14 28.3	-14 ± 7	1.0
38)$N7793$	-17.6	23 55.26	-32 52.1	214 ± 10	3.0
39)$W-L-M$	-13.9	23 59.40	-15 44.6	56 ± 8	1.0

Chapter 5

APPEARANCE OF THE MATTER DISTRIBUTION

Within moving clouds, relying more on intuition
than on vision, step by step I am moving forward.
Reinhold Messner
(1980, Mt. Everest)

This chapter illustrates the possibility of studying general qualitative properties of the processes responsible for the large-scale inhomogeneous distribution of matter using certain features of its present day appearance. One of the most striking of these features is the alleged fractal-type distribution of galaxies and clusters of galaxies at different length scales.

This problem of the most informative characteristics of the matter distribution is closely related to theories of the origin of the observed Universe and is therefore very complicated in its general formulation. Our purpose here is to outline certain possibilities for the search for useful relations.

We consider the possible physical meaning of the measured value of the Hausdorff (fractal) dimension, and in particular, the dependence of this dimension on the dynamical characteristics of the filaments. The observed sheet-like structures are also discussed in the framework of catastrophe theory. However, for a rigorous self-contained treatment we begin with the definitions of some basic terminology.

5.1 Fractals

To describe statistically a set M defined in R^d, Hausdorff introduced a new concept of dimension. Given a positive number α, an external measure l_α of M is introduced in the following way. For a given ρ-covering of the set M, i.e., a covering of M by a countable set of closed balls S_i of radius $r_i < \rho$, first define

$$l_\alpha(M,\rho) = \inf \sum_i r_i^\alpha \; .$$

Then take the limit over all such ρ-coverings as the bounding radius tends to zero

$$l_\alpha(M) = \lim_{\rho \to 0} l_\alpha(M,\rho) \; .$$

The Hausdorff dimension of M is finally determined by the dependence of $l_\alpha(M)$ on α

$$\dim_H M = \sup\{\alpha \mid l_\alpha(M) = \infty\} = \inf\{\alpha \mid l_\alpha(M) = 0\} \; . \qquad (5.1)$$

The Hausdorff dimension of a smooth subset of Euclidean space equals its (integer) topological dimension, i.e., if M is a manifold then

$$\dim_H M = \dim M \; .$$

Mandelbrot introduced the name fractal to denote a set for which $\dim_H M$ is not an integer (Figure 30).

For a set $M \subset R^d$, let $N(M,\rho)$ be the number of balls of radius ρ covering M. The quantity defined by

$$\dim_K M = \limsup_{\rho \to 0} \frac{\ln N(M,\rho)}{\ln(1/\rho)} \qquad (5.2)$$

is called the Kolmogorov capacity. In the case of a compact set one has

$$\dim_H M \leq \dim_K M \; . \qquad (5.3)$$

Let M be a measurable Banach space with $P(M) = 1$. The information dimension of a measure P is defined by

$$\dim_H P = \inf\{\dim_H S \mid S \subset M, \quad P(S) = 1\} \; , \qquad (5.4)$$

where $\dim_H S$ is the Hausdorff dimension of the set S, i.e., the information dimension of P is the minimal Hausdorff dimension that a set of complete measure can have.

Next one comes to the concept of an inhomogeneous fractal, or multifractal. Suppose that $P[B_x(r)]$ is the measure of a ball of radius r and center $x \in M$ and it has the following behavior

$$P[B_x(r)] \sim r^{\alpha(x)} \; , \qquad (5.5)$$

Figure 30 *Fractal.*

or more precisely

$$\lim_{r \to 0} \frac{\ln P[B_x(r)]}{\ln r} = \alpha(x) \ .$$ (5.6)

If the function α is constant, then M is called a homogeneous fractal. If not, the more typical case, it is called an inhomogeneous fractal or multifractal.

To describe the function α consider moments of the measure of balls

$$\langle P[B_x(r)]^q \rangle \sim r^{\phi(q)},$$

or

$$\phi(q) = \lim_{r \to 0} \frac{\ln\langle P[B_x(r)]^q \rangle}{\ln r} \ ,$$

where $\langle f \rangle \equiv P(f) = \int_M f(x) P(dx)$. Using them one can define the Renyi dimensions

$$D_{q+1} \equiv \frac{\phi(q)}{q} \ , \tag{5.7}$$

where

$$D_0 = -\phi(-1)$$

is the Kolmogorov capacity,

$$D_1 = \lim_{q \to 0} \frac{\phi(q)}{q} = \lim_{r \to 0} \frac{\langle \ln P[B_x(r)] \rangle}{\ln r}$$

is the information dimension,

$$D_2 = \phi(1)$$

the correlation dimension, etc.

Since the multifractal nature of the set M is related to range of variation of the function α, one can consider the following partition

$$\Upsilon_\alpha = \{ x \in M \mid \alpha(x) = \alpha \} \ ,$$

and the dimension spectrum $f(\alpha)$ is then defined by

$$f(\alpha) \equiv \dim_H \Upsilon_\alpha, \quad \alpha \in [\alpha_{min}, \alpha_{max}],$$
$$\alpha_{min} = \lim_{q \to +\infty} D_q, \quad \alpha_{max} = \lim_{q \to -\infty} D_q \ .$$

Thus a multifractal is described by the function

$$f : [\alpha_{min}, \alpha_{max}] \to R_+ \ .$$

This is a concave down function with a single maximum value equal to the Kolmogorov capacity D_0

$$\phi(q - 1) = \inf_\alpha \{ \alpha q - f(\alpha) \}$$

hence

$$\inf_\alpha \{ f(\alpha) \} = -\phi(-1) = D_0 \ .$$

An important issue is the relation between the Hausdorff dimension and chaotic properties of dynamical systems, especially the KS-entropy and the Lyapunov characteristic exponents. So far there are no rigorous results on the relation between these quantities in general, but some interesting examples are available.

Consider the set $M(p)$ of all points of the interval $[0,1]$ that contain 1 in their diadic expansions with probability p, $0 \leq p \leq 1$, i.e.,

$$M(p) = \{\omega = 0.\omega_1\omega_2\ldots \mid \omega_k = 0 \text{ or } 1, \lim_{n\to\infty} \frac{1}{n}\sum_{k=1}^{n}\omega_k = p\}.$$

The Lebesque measure of the set $M(1/2)$ (normal numbers) is 1, while if $p \neq 1/2$, its measure is zero. Therefore it is interesting to find the Hausdorff dimension of this set, for it may be the only non-zero characteristic of the set.

It has been proven that

$$\dim_H M(p) = \frac{1}{\ln 2}[-p\ln p - (1-p)\ln(1-p)] \equiv \frac{h}{\ln 2} . \qquad (5.8)$$

Moreover, if one considers the r-adic representation of points in the interval $[0,1]$, i.e.,

$$\omega = \sum_{n=1}^{\infty} \frac{\omega_n}{r^n}, \quad 0 \leq \omega_n \leq r-1 ,$$

and if $N_i(\omega, n)$ denotes the frequency of the presence of i within the set of numbers $\{\omega_n\}$ and

$$0 \leq p_i \leq 1, \quad 0 \leq i \leq r-1, \quad \sum_{i=0}^{r-1} p_i = 1,$$

$$M(p_0, \ldots, p_{r-1}) = \{\omega \mid \lim_{n\to\infty} \frac{N_i(\omega, n)}{n} = p_i; \quad i = 0, \ldots, r-1\}$$

then

$$\dim_H M(p_0, \ldots, p_{r-1}) = \left(-\sum_{i=0}^{r-1} p_i \ln p_i\right) / \ln r \equiv \frac{h}{\ln r} . \qquad (5.9)$$

Recalling that for the Bernoulli shift B

$$h(B) = -\sum_{i=0}^{r-1} p_i \ln p_i, \qquad (5.10)$$

where r is the number of possible states and p_i the corresponding probability, then one readily has the relation between KS-entropy (h) and the Hausdorff dimension $(\dim_H M)$. In particular one can see that the Hausdorff dimension of $M \subset [0,1]$ reflects the degree of uncertainty in choosing a point from M.

One can use this result to calculate the Hausdorff dimension of the Cantor set, for example. Let us recall that the latter is formed by excluding the closed interval $[1/3, 2/3]$ from $[0,1]$, then $[1/9, 2/9]$ from $[0, 1/3]$, etc. Now note that the Cantor set is the set of points with 3-adic representation not containing the number 1, i.e., the set $M(1/2, 0, 1/2)$, $r = 3$, therefore

$$\dim_H M = \frac{\ln 2}{\ln 3} \ .$$

Kaplan-Yorke Conjecture. For dissipative systems the following quantity

$$\dim_\Lambda M = k + \frac{\lambda_1 + \ldots + \lambda_k}{|\lambda_{k+1}|} \tag{5.11}$$

is called the Lyapunov dimension, where

$$k = \max\{i \mid \lambda_1 + \ldots + \lambda_i > 0\} \ ,$$

and

$$\lambda_1 > \lambda_2 > \ldots > \lambda_{max}$$

are Lyapunov characteristic exponents defined by

$$\lambda(x, v) \equiv \limsup_{t \to \infty} \frac{\ln \|df_x^t(v)\|}{t} \ . \tag{5.12}$$

In the case of arbitrary strange attractors Kaplan and Yorke proposed the following conjecture

$$\dim_H M = \dim_\Lambda M \ .$$

The following inequality is known to hold only for ergodic systems on M

$$\dim_H M \leq \dim_\Lambda M \ . \tag{5.13}$$

Presumably, in the general case one should not hope to have a formula relating the Hausdorff dimension only to the Lyapunov exponents.

To complete this discussion let us also state a well-known result, the Pesin formula, which relates the KS-entropy to the Lyapunov exponents

$$h(f) = \int_M \sum_{\lambda_i(x) > 0} \lambda_i(x) P(dx) \ . \tag{5.14}$$

5.2   Hausdorff Dimension and Physical Characteristics of the Filaments.

As mentioned above, one of the most remarkable features of the matter distribution in the Universe appears to be its so-called fractal nature. The possibility of representing the two-point correlation function for galaxies and their clusters as a power law function of the radius (Figure 31)

$$\xi(r) \propto r^{-\gamma}, \quad \gamma = 1.8 \,, \tag{5.15}$$

is usually interpreted as evidence of a fractal distribution with Hausdorff dimension

$$\dim_H = 3 - \gamma = 1.2 \,. \tag{5.16}$$

There are indications of other power indices on different length scales. What physical processes can be responsible for this phenomenon and which cannot? What direct information on the parameters of filaments can the value of the power law index give? Below we consider these questions again using an approach based on the theory of dynamical systems.

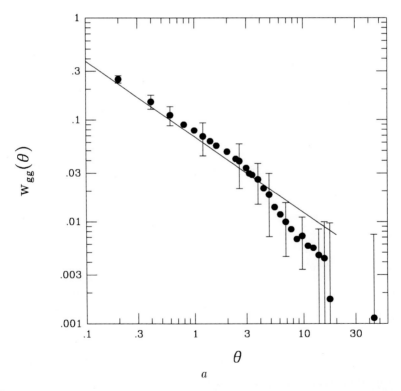

a

Figure 31 *a) The angular 2-point galaxy correlation function estimated from the Lick catalogue containing about 10^6 galaxies. Errors are estimated from different regions of the sky. The straight line represents the power law $\theta^{-0.8}$;*

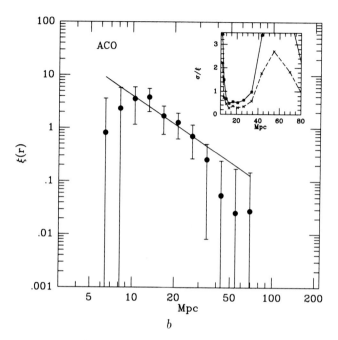

Figure 31 *(Continued)*

b) The spatial 2-point correlation function for galaxy clusters from the Abell, Corwin and Olowin catalogue. Error bars are estimated using the bootstrap resampling technique. The straight line represents the power law $(r/r_0)^{-1.8}$, with an amplitude $r_0 = 20\,Mpc$. The inner plot shows the noise to signal ratio as a function of the cluster separation. The continuous line is for bootstrap errors while the dashed line is for quasi-Poissonian errors (both diagrams are by M. Plionis).

Consider a flow $\{f^t\}$ on a smooth compact manifold X of (topological) dimension d (see Chapter 2). The trajectory of an n-dimensional ($n < d$) submanifold A in X is the set

$$\Gamma(A) = \{f^t(A) \mid t \in R\} . \tag{5.17}$$

For a typical flow, such a trajectory $\Gamma(A)$ locally has $(n + 1)$-dimensions, but the dimension can be different globally due to the complexity of the trajectory. This complexity, as we saw above, is described by the Hausdorff dimension.

Clearly this dimension must lie between the local dimension of the trajectory and the dimension of the manifold X

$$n + 1 \leq \dim_H \Gamma(A) \leq d .$$

For example, in the case of a point $(n = 0)$

$$1 \leq \dim_H \Gamma(A) \leq d .$$

If in this case Γ is the trajectory of a typical dynamical ergodic system on the space X, then this trajectory is everywhere dense on X and therefore $\dim_H \Gamma(A) = d$.

The typical finite trajectory

$$\Gamma_T(A) = \{f^t(A) \mid t \in [0, T]\} ,$$

because of its complexity, independent of A, will have a Hausdorff dimension greater than 1 but less than d.

The difference from the limiting values (1 and d) depends on the chaotic properties of f and on the value of T. For completely mixed systems $\dim_H \Gamma_T(A)$ should tend to d, while for an unmixed system (due to weak mixing properties and/or the time T) it will be close to 1. For K-systems the Shennon-McMillan-Breiman theorem guarantees the uniform exponential rate of loss of information. Due to this fact the Hausdorff dimension of such a system is approximately

$$\dim_H \Gamma_T(A) \simeq d \cdot (1 - (d - 1)/d \cdot \exp(-T/\tau)) , \qquad (5.18)$$

where τ is the mixing time scale.

Before turning to galaxies and their clusters let us recall some results of investigations of gravitating systems as dynamical systems. It has been shown that N-body self-gravitating systems possess strong chaotic properties, in certain cases even those of peculiar to Kolmogorov systems with exponential deviation of geodesics in phase space and therefore with exponential loss of information. In accord with results of ergodic theory this implies the tending by the system to cover smoothly the energy hypersurface (relaxation).

The corresponding time scale for spherical gravitating systems equals

$$\tau = \left(\frac{15}{4}\right)^{2/3} \frac{v}{2\pi\sqrt{2G M \rho^{2/3}}} . \qquad (5.19)$$

where v, ρ and M are the mean velocity dispersion, number density and masses of the self-gravitating bodies.

For the typical parameters of clusters of galaxies that time scale yields

$$\tau \simeq 10^{11}(v/500km/s)(\rho/50Mpc^{-3})^{-2/3}(M/10^{10}M_\odot)^{-1}yrs . \qquad (5.20)$$

This means that clusters of galaxies in general cannot be mixed yet, as also follows from other studies. The observed Hausdorff dimension is $\dim_H \Gamma = 1.2$, again indicating that these systems are far from being completely mixed, as follows from Eq. (5.18).

When $T/\tau \ll 1$, Eq. (5.18) has the form

$$\dim_H \Gamma_T = 1 + (d - 1)T/\tau . \tag{5.21}$$

Thus Eq. (5.18) provides a formula for the Hausdorff dimension $\dim_H \Gamma_T$, based on the calculation of the expression (5.19) for the time scale of the filaments.

These conclusions readily lead to consequences which can be tested with observations. Note in particular that in the case of a less mixed cluster, Eq. (5.18) provides a constraint for the combination of the age of the Universe and the parameters M, v and ρ of the clusters. The value of the Hausdorff dimension can be obtained from Eq. (5.18) for a given class of systems through investigation of their dynamical properties, namely, by estimating the time scale Eq. (5.19).

For clusters with stochastic dynamics the Hausdorff dimension represented by the two-point correlation function should be close to d, while for non-stochastic ones the Hausdorff dimension is close to 1.

The closeness of $\dim_H \Gamma_T$ to 1 (and not to 2 or 3) may reflect the fact that stochastic motion most probably has occurred not in a three-space, but on a two-surface. This conclusion can be considered as supporting the viewpoint which considers galaxies to be distributed on the sheet-like surfaces of voids, formed, say by the Ostriker-Cowie-Ikeuchi explosion mechanism.

Similarly, the indication of $\dim_H = 2.2$ on larger scales of the galaxy distribution (perhaps up to $30h^{-1}Mpc$) might imply that the basic process responsible for that structure has occurred in 3-space. Hence the nature of the processes on different scales may be different. Eventually, the multifractal tendency of the distribution of filaments, already supported by observational data, seems to be quite natural.

Finally, we mention the importance of another fractal dimension $\dim_H^6$ of the 6-dimensional (x, v) space instead of $\dim_H \equiv \dim_H^3$ of the 3-dimensional (x) space, considering the possibility of representing the correlation function $\zeta(x, v)$ by an expression with a power law dependence on the 6-radius

$$\zeta(x, v) \propto R^{-(6-\dim_H^6)} , \tag{5.22}$$

where

$$R^2 = r^2 + v^2, \qquad r^2 = x^2 + y^2 + z^2, \qquad v^2 = v_x^2 + v_y^2 + v_z^2,$$

i.e., corresponding to the existence of a fractal structure in that space.

Consider the case when dissipative systems play the primary role in the formation of filamentary structure. Then recalling the Kaplan-Yorke conjecture one can arrive at a general conclusion about the nature of the dissipative processes and hence the structure of the final configurations.

For example, when

$$1 < \dim_H^6 < 2$$

or

$$2 < \dim_H^6 < 3$$

then

$$k = 1 \ , \quad \lambda_1 > 0 \ , \quad \lambda_1 + \lambda_2 < 0 \ ,$$

$$k = 2 \ , \quad \lambda_1 + \lambda_2 > 0 \ , \quad \lambda_1 + \lambda_2 + \lambda_3 < 0 \ ,$$

respectively. In the first case the attracting set can only be a line (string), in the second—a surface or a line (Figure 32).

Thus if one considers the fractal structure of the distribution of galaxies and clusters to be an established fact, then the values of the dimensions $\dim_H^3$ and especially of $\dim_H^6$ lead to some general information about the processes responsible for it.

5.3 Sheet-Like Structures as Elementary Catastrophes

Consider the behavior of the motion of matter on the spatial 3-manifold M of the Universe described by a one-parameter map of the form

$$g^t : M \to M : x \mapsto x + tv(x) \ .$$

When $v = \mathrm{grad} S$, where $S \in \mathcal{F}M$, this is known as the Zeldovich map (Figure 33).

Let us study the state of matter at some fixed time t if the initial conditions at some time 0 are given. It is not difficult to convince oneself that the problem in this formulation involves catastrophe theory. Indeed, identify the points of manifold M at time t with the space of states and those at the initial time with the space of control parameters. The problem thus amounts to the search for catastrophes admitted in the control space M.

According to Thom's theorem the type of catastrophes depends on the dimension of n. Since one has $n = 3$ for the Universe, the typical catastrophes can be of the following types: fold, cusp (double cusp), swallowtail, hyperbolic and elliptic umbilics.

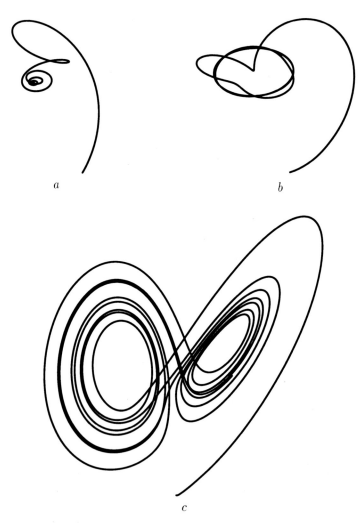

Figure 32   *Attracting sets at a) $k = 0$, b) $k = 1$, and c) $k = 2$.*

An important concept for our purposes is that of a caustic. This is defined in terms of the generating function $F = F(x, c)$ as a hypersurface $\Delta \subset R^{n+k}$ which consists of the critical values of the map

$$(x, c) \mapsto (y = \partial F / \partial x, c) .$$

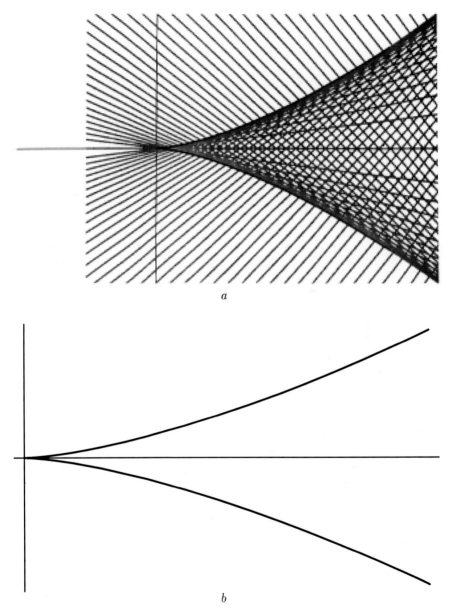

a

b

Figure 33 *Zeldovich map (a) and cusp (b).*

In our problem the caustics represent the sets of singular points of the matter density, i.e., of infinite values of the latter as shown in Figures 34, 35.

Since we actually observe two-projections of the catastrophes, the problem is reduced to the comparison of the sheet-like dense configurations of matter with the caustics predicted in a classification of elementary catastrophes. Consider as an illustration the slices of the distribution of galaxies in Figure 36. In Figure 36a traces of several catastrophes are clearly seen. Some of them can also be followed in other slices. The crucial problem is to clarify the three-geometry of these structures in the sequence of slices with a more complete set of data. Only then can one have a clear image of the possible types of catastrophes and hence on the possible evolutionary paths of the filaments. In particular, it is interesting to find out whether there exist structures corresponding to more complex, namely, swallowtail

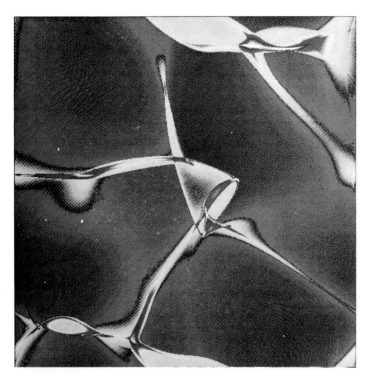

Figure 34 *Caustic pattern during high resolution 3D calculations to simulate the formation of filaments according to the Zeldovich pancake theory. The colours indicate logarithmic changes of density (from T. Buchert and M. Bartelmann, Astr. Ap., vol.251, p.389, 1989).*

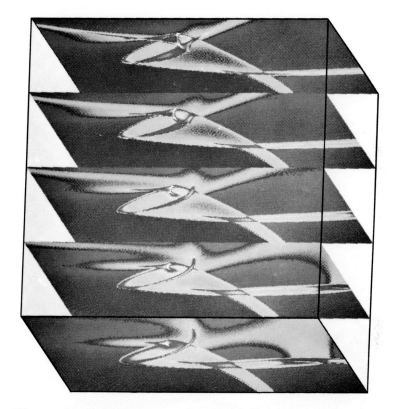

Figure 35 *A slicing of a simulated 3D-cube of the previous figure.*

or umbilic type catastrophes as expected according to theory in the case of three control parameters.

Along with pure geometric features, the law of increase of the density in approaching the caustics can also be useful in determining the allowed types of catastrophes. The following results are available for the mean density within some volume:

$$A_2 : \qquad \rho \sim l^{-1/3};$$
$$A_{\pm 3} : \qquad \rho \sim l^{-2/3};$$
$$A_4 : \qquad \rho \sim l^{-3/4};$$
$$D_{+4} : \qquad \rho \sim l^{-1};$$
$$D_{-4} : \qquad \rho \sim l^{-1}.$$

This approach can be a rather useful way to analyze the data of the deep redshift surveys.

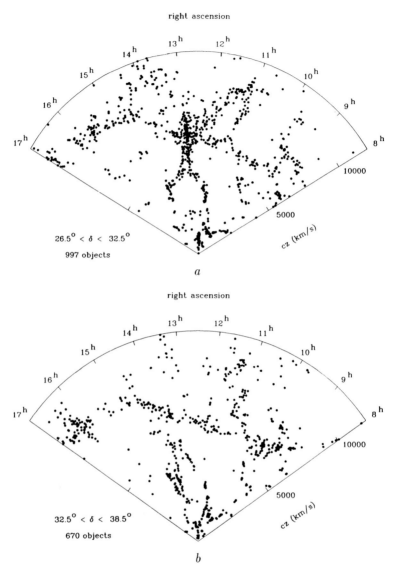

Figure 36 *Three slices from the Center for Astrophysics (CfA) redshift survey for galaxies with $m_{B(0)} \leq 15.5$ and $cz \leq 12.000 kms^{-1}$ (by V. de Lapparent, M. Geller and J. Huchra, 1988).*

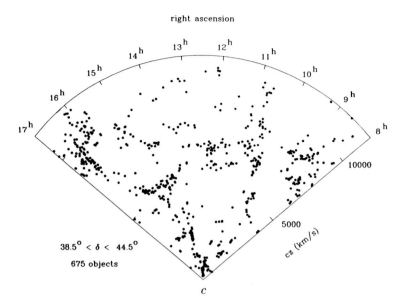

Figure 36 *(Continued)*

Bibliography

The Hausdorff dimension was introduced in:

[1] Hausdorff F., Dimension und Ausseres Mass, *Math. Ann.*, **79**, p.157, 1919;

Many properties of fractals illustrated by numerous explicit examples are given in:

[2] Mandelbrot B.B., *The Fractal Geometry of Nature*, Freeman, N.Y.,1983.

[3] Bunde A. and Havlin S. (Eds.) *Fractals and Disordered Systems*, Springer-Verlag, 1991.

The relation of Hausdorff dimension to Lyapunov exponents (Kaplan-Yorke conjecture) was considered in:

[4] Kaplan J.L. and Yorke J.A., Numerical Solution of a Generalized Eigenvalue Problem for Even Mapping, *Functional Differential Equations and Approximation of a Fixed Point* Lecture Notes in Mathematics, **730**, Springer-Verlag, 1979;

and to KS-entropy in:

[5] Billingsley P., *Ergodic Theory and Information*, 1969.

Different aspects of the fractal distribution of galaxies are discussed in:

[6] Calzetti D., Giavalisco M., and Ruffini R., The Normalization of the Correlation Functions for Extragalactic Structures, *Astr. Ap.*, **198**, p.1, 1988.

[7] Jones B.J.T., Martinez V.J., Saar E., and Einasto J., Multifractal Description of the Large-Scale Structure of the Universe, *Ap. J.*, **332**, p.L1, 1988.

[8] Balian R, Schaeffer R., Scale-Invariant Matter Distribution in the Universe. II. Bifractal Behaviour, *Astr. Ap.*, **226**, p.373, 1989.

[9] Coleman P.H., Pietronero L., The Fractal Structure of the Universe, *Phys. Rep.*, **213**, p.311, 1992.

The Shennon-McMillan-Breiman theorem can be found in:

[10] Martin N.F.G. and England J.W., *Mathematical Theory of Entropy*, Addison-Wesley Publ., 1981.

The relation between Hausdorff dimension and dynamical characteristics of clusters of galaxies is derived in:

[11] Gurzadyan V.G. and Kocharyan A.A., On the Nature of the Fractal Structure of the Universe, *Europhys.Lett.*, **15**, p.801, 1991.

Its observational consequences for 4 rich Abell clusters are reported in:

[12] Monaco P., Observational Support for the Gurzadyan-Kocharyan Relation in Clusters of Galaxies, *Astr. Ap.*, 1994 (submitted).

Exponential instability of N-body gravitating systems was shown and the characteristic time scale was derived in:

[13] Gurzadyan V.G. and Savvidy G.K., On the Problem of Relaxation of Stellar Systems, *Doklady AN SSSR*, **277**, p.69, 1984;

[14] Gurzadyan V.G. and Savvidy G.K., Collective Relaxation of Stellar Systems, *Astr. Ap.*, **160**, p.203, 1986.

These results were used, e.g., for the analysis of the data on 127 star clusters:

[15] Vesperini E., Possible Observational Support for Gurzadyan-Savvidy Relaxation for Globular Clusters, *Astr. Ap.*, **266**, p.215, 1992.

The properties of the observed matter structures, particularly in the context of Zeldovich pancake theory, were considered by means of catastrophe theory in:

[16] Arnold V.I., Shandarin S.F., and Zeldovich Ya.B., The large Scale Structure of the Universe. I. General Properties. One and Two Dimensional Models, *Geophys. Astrophys. Fluid. Dyn.*, **20**, p.111, 1982.

Chapter 6

STATISTICAL METHODS

If we begin at once to break the ties
that bind us to nature and to devote ourselves
purely to combination of pure color and independent form,
we shall produce works which are mere geometric design,
resembling something like a necktie or a carpet.
Wassily Kandinsky

In this chapter we review the principal methods which are widely used in the statistical investigation of the distribution of galaxies at large length scales. All of these approaches are purely positional and neglect

a. the dynamical data, namely data on the peculiar velocities and large scale streaming effects, etc., and

b. the Newtonian character of the interaction between galaxies.

Although correlation functions remain the most popular tool, a number of other approaches are used as well. Among these are methods involving topological measures, the minimal-spanning-tree technique, and the wavelet transform, all of which will be introduced below. To avoid straying too far from the goals we are addressing in the present geometrical approach, we will not discuss other methods which are also being used such as percolation, void probability functions, elongation statistics, etc., nor the various biases and other difficulties which arise in their application and the ways of overcoming them.

6.1 Correlation Functions

Correlation analysis is one of the most important methods used in the investigation of the statistical dependence between random variables, and is often used in many fields. Moreover, as indicated above, correlation functions also provide useful information about dynamical systems, although often being difficult to work with in practice.

The popularity of the correlation function formalism in the analysis of the large scale structure of the Universe over the last several decades is mostly due to the first observation. However, for us its relationship to dynamical systems is also important, especially in view of the discussion of the properties of the CMB below in Chapter 8.

Consider the following process. N pointlike objects are to be distributed in some way in a 3-space V. The problem is to describe the statistical relationships among the positions of these objects.

The probability of finding one object within a volume element dV at a given position can be represented by

$$dP = ndV \; , \qquad (6.1)$$

where n is the mean number density of objects averaged over volume after N events. n does not depend on the coordinates and direction, since the distribution is assumed to be isotropic and homogeneous. The probability of finding two points in a pair of volume elements dV_1 and dV_2, respectively, at two positions separated by a distance r_{12} is given by

$$dP = n^2 dV_1 dV_2 [1 + \xi(r_{12})] \; , \qquad (6.2)$$

where $\xi(r_{12})$ is called the two-point spatial correlation function. Again due to the homogeneity of the distribution these quantities only depend on the relative distance between the two positions. For the number of objects within some average ball B, one has

$$< N > = n^2 [\int_B (1 + \xi(r)) dV] \; .$$

In the case of a Poisson process the two-point correlation function vanishes

$$\xi(r) = 0 \; .$$

From the point of view of ergodic theory such a random distribution implies complete statistical independence and corresponds to a distribution produced by dynamical processes of Bernoulli shift type, which are the maximally chaotic systems. In every other case one must have systems with weaker statistical properties, such as systems with various degrees of mixing.

In the case of a positive correlation between the locations of a pair of objects, one has

$$\xi > 0 ,$$

but the negative values

$$-1 \leq \xi < 0 ,$$

when there is an anticorrelation. Thus the correlation function determines the departure of the process from a completely random one.

The main information known about the actual distribution of galaxies, however, does not include their 3-coordinates, but is obtained from two-dimensional surveys. Therefore to determine the spatial correlation function $\xi(r)$, one must first obtain the angular correlation function.

The two-point angular correlation function $\omega(\vartheta_{12})$ can be defined analogously

$$dp = \mathcal{N}^2 d\Omega_1 d\Omega_2[1 + \omega(\vartheta_{12})] , \tag{6.3}$$

and represents the probability of finding a pair of objects within the celestial angle elements $d\Omega_1$ and $d\Omega_2$ at two angular positions separated by an angular distance ϑ_{12}. Here $\mathcal{N}$ is the mean surface number density of objects.

We now derive the formula connecting the spatial correlation function to the angular one. This is accomplished by decomposing the volume differential $dV = r^2 dr d\Omega$ into the radial differential and the angular solid angle differential $d\Omega$ and integrating over the radial variable. Consider the probability of finding an object within the angular solid angle element $d\Omega$, expressed in terms of the surface density $\mathcal{N}$

$$dp = \mathcal{N} d\Omega . \tag{6.4}$$

To obtain this one must integrate over the contributions to this probability from the differential volume elements which project onto $d\Omega$

$$dp = \int \frac{dP}{dr} dr = n d\Omega \int r^2 dr , \tag{6.5}$$

leading to the identification

$$\mathcal{N} = n \int r^2 dr .$$

Rewriting the expression for the probability of finding two objects within two given volume elements dV_1 and dV_2 leads to

$$dP(dV_1, dV_2) = n^2[1 + \xi(r_{12})]r_1^2 r_2^2 d\Omega_1 d\Omega_2 dr_1 dr_2 ,$$

so that after integration over the radial variables to obtain the angular probability dP, one can make the identification

$$\mathcal{N}^2\omega(\vartheta) = n^2 \int \xi(r_{12}) r_1^2 r_2^2 dr_1 dr_2 .$$

This gives us the following relation between the angular and spatial correlation functions

$$\omega(\vartheta) = \frac{\int \xi(r_{12}) r_1^2 r_2^2 dr_1 dr_2}{[\int r^2 dr]^2} .$$

Introducing the new radial variables

$$u = (r_1 - r_2)/2 , \qquad y = (r_1 + r_2)/2 ,$$
$$r_1 = y + u/2 , \qquad r_2 = y - u/2 ,$$

leads to the equivalent expression

$$\omega(\vartheta) = \frac{\int (y^2 + \frac{u^2}{4})^2 \xi(\sqrt{u^2 + 2(y^2 + \frac{u^2}{4})(1 - \cos\vartheta)}) dy du}{[\int y^2 dy]^2} .$$

In the limit

$$|u| \ll y, \; (\Leftrightarrow |r_1 - r_2| \ll (r_1 + r_2)/2), \qquad \vartheta \ll 1 \;\rightarrow\; 2(1 - \cos\vartheta) \approx \vartheta^2 ,$$

i.e., when the relative distance between the two objects is much smaller than their distances from the observer, the above equation simplifies to

$$\omega(\vartheta) = \frac{\int y^4 \xi(\sqrt{u^2 + y^2\vartheta^2}) dy du}{[\int y^2 dy]^2} . \tag{6.6}$$

Attributing a statistical weight $\varphi(r)$ to the radial coordinate r will change dr as follows:

$$dr_i \rightarrow \varphi(r_i) dr_i .$$

The last equation becomes

$$\omega(\vartheta) = \frac{\int r_1^2 r_2^2 \varphi(r_1)\varphi(r_2)\xi(r_{12}) dr_1 dr_2}{[\int \varphi(r) r^2 dr]^2} .$$

or in terms of the new variables (u, y) in the same approximation as Eq. (6.6) one has

$$\omega(\vartheta) = \frac{\int y^4 \varphi(y)\xi(\sqrt{u^2 + y^2\vartheta^2}) dy du}{[\int \varphi^2(y) y^2 dy]^2} . \tag{6.7}$$

This equation is known as the Limber equation. The function $\varphi(r)$ describes the contribution of the galaxy luminosity function.

In the most important case the two-point correlation function $\xi(r)$ can be represented by a power law function

$$\xi(r) \propto r^{-\gamma} ,$$

so one immediately finds from the Limber equation the following behavior for the two-point angular correlation function

$$\omega(\vartheta) \propto \vartheta \frac{1}{\vartheta^{\gamma}} \propto \vartheta^{1-\gamma} .$$

Finally we consider an example showing the relation between the Kolmogorov capacity of a set and the correlation function, which can also be of interest in connection with the problem of the distribution of galaxies. Suppose a ball S_{ε} of radius ε contains a given object in a compact subset M of R^3. Express the probability of finding the object within a volume element in the spherical form

$$dP = \rho(r)drd\Omega .$$

Since

$$V = 4\pi \int_M \rho(r)dr ,$$

one has

$$N(\varepsilon) = V/ \int_0^{\varepsilon} \rho(r)dr ,$$

where $N(\varepsilon)$ is the number of balls of radius ε within the M.

Now calculate the Kolmogorov capacity of M. From the definition Eq. (5.2)

$$\dim_K M = \lim_{\varepsilon \to 0} \frac{\ln N(\varepsilon)}{\ln(1/\varepsilon)} = \lim_{\varepsilon \to 0} \frac{\ln \int_0^{\varepsilon} \rho(r)dr}{\ln \varepsilon} = \lim_{\varepsilon \to 0} \frac{\varepsilon\rho(\varepsilon)}{\int_0^{\varepsilon} \rho(r)dr} = 1+\lim_{\varepsilon \to 0} \frac{\varepsilon\rho\,'(\varepsilon)}{\rho(\varepsilon)} ,$$

where L'Hopital's rule was used. When the density has a power law behavior

$$\rho(r) \propto r^{\alpha} ,$$

one obtains

$$\dim_K M = 1 + \alpha .$$

When instead it behaves like the sum of two power law expressions

$$\rho(r) \propto r^{\alpha} + r^{\beta} ,$$

one obtains

$$\frac{\varepsilon\rho\,'(\varepsilon)}{\rho(\varepsilon)} = \frac{\alpha\varepsilon^{\alpha} + \beta\varepsilon^{\beta}}{\varepsilon^{\alpha} + \varepsilon^{\beta}} ,$$

i.e., the Kolmogorov capacity only depends on the smaller power index

$$\dim_K M = 1 + \min\{\alpha, \beta\} \; . \tag{6.8}$$

When the probability is of the form

$$dP = (1 + \xi)r^2 dr d\Omega \; ,$$

where $\xi \propto r^{-\gamma}$, one can make the identification

$$\rho = r^2 + \xi r^2 \propto r^2 + r^{2-\gamma} \; ,$$

leading to the result

$$\dim_K M = 3 - \gamma \; . \tag{6.9}$$

6.2 Topological Measures

An important aspect of the investigation of the distribution of matter on large scales is the possibility of understanding its topology. Using concepts well known in topology to quantitatively describe filaments therefore seems to be a natural thing to do. Furthermore, the language and constructs of topology enable one to adopt a terminology which can distinguish the various properties of a cellular, inhomogeneous distribution of galaxies.

Consider a set of pointlike objects distributed in some way in R^3, described by a smooth density function $\rho(\mathbf{r})$ on R^3. Consider the level surfaces of this function

$$M_c = \{\mathbf{r} \in R^3 \mid \rho(\mathbf{r}) = c\} \; .$$

The Euclidean metric of R^3

$$\delta = dx^2 + dy^2 + dz^2$$

induces a metric g and corresponding Levi-Civita connection on the each such manifold M_c.

According to the Gauss-Bonnet theorem for any compact 2-dimensional manifold (surface) M_c in R^3 one has the relation

$$T_c \equiv \int_{M_c} K(\det g)^{1/2} dx^1 \wedge dx^2 = 4\pi(1 - h) \; ,$$

where

$$K = R/2$$

is the Gaussian curvature (R is the scalar curvature) and h the genus of the surface. The latter is equal to the number of holes or handles of the surface.

It is remarkable that the integral T_c does not depend on the metric g, i.e., is a topological, rather than a geometrical quantity. For example, its value is 4π ($h = 0$) for any sphere or ellipsoid, 0 ($h = 1$) for a torus or a cup, -4π ($h = 2$) for a sphere with two handles, etc.

Therefore the distribution of the set of points defined by T_c or equivalently T_c/v_c, where

$$v_c = vol(\{\mathbf{r} \in R^3 \mid \rho(\mathbf{r}) \le c\})$$

and the volume of any region N is

$$vol(N) = \int_N dx \wedge dy \wedge dz .$$

Now consider the fluctuation

$$\Delta(\mathbf{r}) \equiv (\rho(\mathbf{r}) - \bar{\rho})/\bar{\rho}$$

of the density with respect to its mean value

$$\bar{\rho} = \int \rho(\mathbf{r}) dV / \int dV .$$

For Gaussian density fluctuations

$$f(\Delta) = \frac{1}{\sigma\sqrt{2\pi}} exp\left(-\frac{\Delta^2}{2\sigma^2}\right) ,$$

one obtains the following formula

$$T_c = -\frac{1}{\pi}\left[-\frac{\xi''(0)}{\xi(0)}\right]^{3/2} (1 - \nu^2) exp(-\nu^2/2), \tag{6.10}$$

where

$$\xi''(0) = d^2\xi(r)/dr^2 \mid_{r=0}$$

is the second derivative of two-point spatial correlation function and

$$\nu = \Delta(c)/\sqrt{\xi(0)}$$

is the density expressed in units of standard deviations from the mean.

A necessary condition here is to look for scales exceeding the correlation length, so that

$$\xi(\mid \mathbf{r}_1 - \mathbf{r}_2 \mid) = \langle\Delta(\mathbf{r}_1)\Delta(\mathbf{r}_2)\rangle \ll 1.$$

It is easy to see that the function T_c is in fact the second derivative of a Gaussian function and hence is symmetric about $\nu = 0$.

Calculating the resulting function T_c for a given sample set of points and comparing it with this symmetric curve leads to a quantitative measure of the departure from a Gaussian distribution. The following terminology has been introduced to distinguish the various possible topological structures which have been found

Swiss cheese or bubble: predominance of isolated voids (right shift with respect to the symmetric curve),
Sponge: symmetric, interchangeable voids and clusters (no shift),
Meatball: predominance of isolated clusters (left shift).

Among other topological measures which have also been proposed to describe the filamentary structure is the $2D$ analog of Euler-Poincare characteristics.

This method has been applied to the CfA and other catalogues and indicates closeness to a sponge-like topology. However, the problem of the sensitivity of the method to slightly differing initial conditions and hence to observational effects seems to be important.

6.3   Minimal Spanning Tree

The minimal-spanning-tree approach, which tries to identify the filaments from a set of N points distributed on a 2-surface, is based on the methods of graph theory. The idea is to reduce the set of such points to a graph and to study the graph. This technique involves the following three steps (Figure 37).

1. *Construction of a tree graph.*

Construct a minimal connected graph, i.e., connect all N points (vertices) with lines (edges) in such a way as to minimize the total length of their continuous sequence (path). If the degree of a node is defined to be the number of edges starting from it, then define a branch to be the sequence of edges connecting a node of degree 1 to a node of degree exceeding 2 with all intermediate ones of degree 2. The tree with no loops (circuits) and with the minimum total edge length is called the minimal spanning tree.

2. *Pruning.*

All edges connecting nodes of degree 1 and those of degree 2 are removed. As a result of this operation only the nodes belonging to the branch remain.

3. *Separation.*

All edges with length exceeding some critical value are removed.

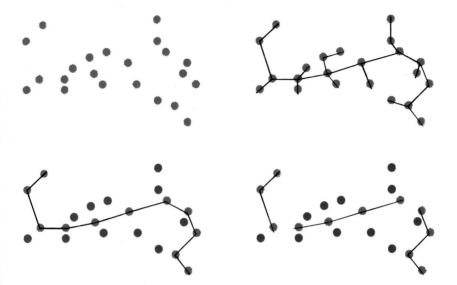

Figure 37 *Spanning tree steps.*

These procedures enable one to distinguish configurations of points whose distribution differs from a random one. Numerical studies indicate no evidence for branches in the case of a Poisson distribution of points. The minimal-spanning-tree method has been applied, in particular, to the data of the CfA catalogue and to the Abell clusters (Figure 38) and certain filaments were identified.

6.4 Wavelet Transform

The wavelet transform method has been successfully used in various problems where one must study the properties of an uncertain signal. The idea of the method is to analyze the decomposition of a signal in terms of certain elementary signals called wavelets. The signal may be a function of the time or of spatial variables.

Consider a signal $s(x)$ in the form

$$s(x) = \int \psi(x, a) w(x, a) d\mu(a) \ ,$$

where $\psi(x, a)$ are wavelet coefficients and $w(x, a)$ is the wavelet, while a represents the parameter determining the wavelet family. The problem in a given application is how to choose the wavelets. This choice depends on

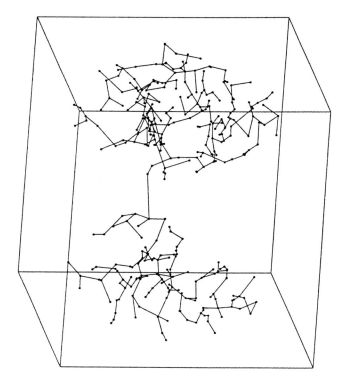

Figure 38 *Minimal Spanning tree for a sample of Abell clusters (from M. Plionis, R. Valdarnini and Y.P. Jing, Astrophys. J., vol.398, p.12, 1992).*

the goals of the application. In particular, it is convenient to use affine transformations to analyze structural characteristics of the signal. In this case the wavelets should be invariant with respect to affine transformations. As is well known, the basic operations of affine transformations are

   a) translation

$$g(t) \rightarrow g(t - b)$$

and

   b) dilation, i.e., the change of scale

$$g(t) \rightarrow \frac{1}{\sqrt{a}} g(\frac{t}{a}).$$

Invariant functions are those with zero mean

$$\int w(x, a) d\mu(a) = 0 .$$

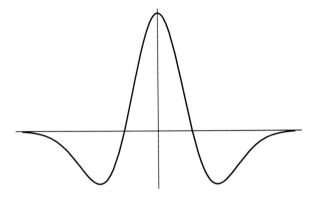

Figure 39 *1D Mexican hat.*

A frequently used wavelet fulfilling these conditions is the so-called Mexican hat function (Figure 39)

$$w(x,a) = (1 - x^2/a^2)\exp(-x^2/2a^2)\,,$$

which is the second derivative of the Gaussian function, and in the $2D$ case the radial Mexican hat function (Figure 40,Figure 41,Figure 42)

$$w(x,y,a) = (2 - (x^2 + y^2)/a^2)\exp(-(x^2 + y^2)/2a^2)\,.$$

Other wavelets can be used as well, for example, piecewise constant or complex ones. Well known among the latter is the Morlet wavelet (Figure 43)

$$w(x,\Omega,t) = e^{-i\Omega x - t^2/2} - \sqrt{2}e^{-\Omega^2/4 + i\Omega x - t^2}\,.$$

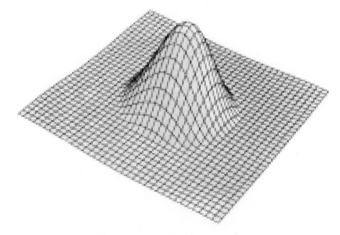

Figure 40 *2D Mexican hat.*

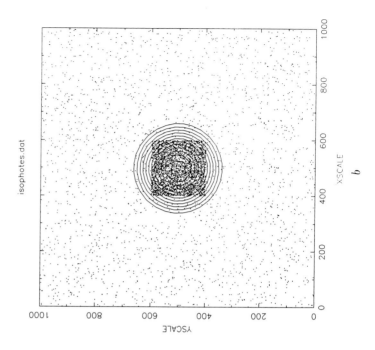

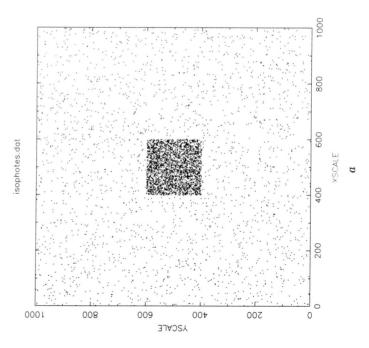

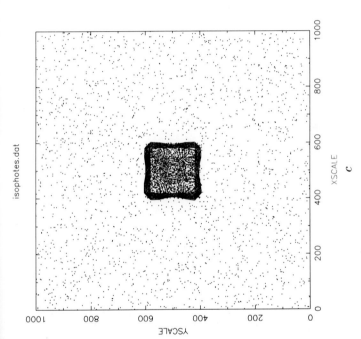

Figure 41 Mexican Hat detecting structures: (a) squared structure in a uniform 2D distribution of galaxies; (b) wavelet detects the structure: iso-contours of the wavelet coefficients; (c) the square shape of the structure given by circular wavelet (by E. Escalera).

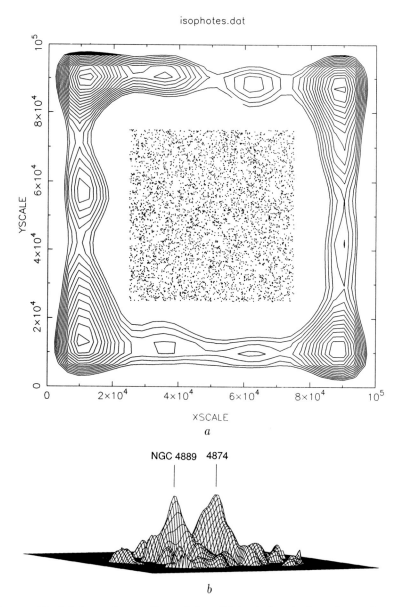

Figure 42 *(a) Isocontours of wavelet coefficients for the transform of a uniform distribution of galaxies; (b) Isosurface of wavelet coefficients for the Coma cluster of galaxies. Peaks denote the cluster core (by E. Escalera).*

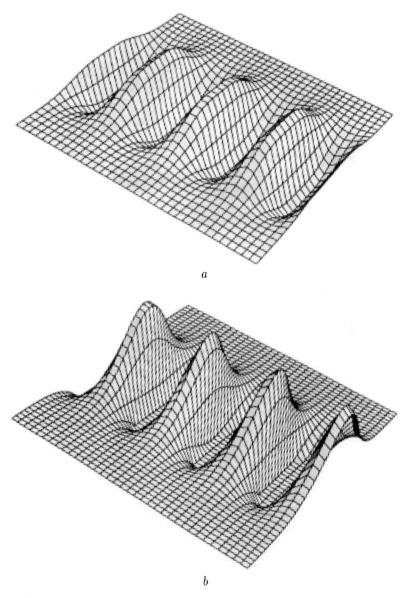

a

b

Figure 43 *(a) Real and (b) imaginary parts of the Morlet wavelet.*

In applying this method to the analysis of the distribution of galaxies one must choose the distribution function and the scaling parameter a. If the former does not depend on the wavelet method, the second may be freely chosen in the study.

This method can be especially useful for the study of galaxy clustering if is used together with other statistical methods.

Bibliography

The history of serious consideration of the correlation function formalism in astrophysics dates back to the 40's, when the problem of correlation of the brightness of the Milky Way in two close directions was formulated:

[1] Ambartsumian V.A., On the Problem of the Fluctuations of Brightness of the Milky Way, *Comm. Acad. Sci. of Armenia*, **1**, p.9, 1944.

This approach found further development in the series of papers by Chandrasekhar and Munch, including:

[2] Chandrasekhar S. and Munch G., The Theory of the Fluctuations in Brightness of the Milky Way.V., *Ap. J.*, **115**, p.103, 1952;

and later led to the derivation of Limber's integral equation:

[3] Limber D.N., The Analysis of Counts of the Extragalactic Nebulae in Terms of a Fluctuating Density Field, *Ap. J.*, **117**, p.134, 1953.

A detailed description of correlation function techniques is contained in:

[4] Peebles P.J.E., *The Large-Scale Structure of the Universe*, Princeton University Press, Princeton, 1980.

These topological concepts have been first used in this field by:

[5] Doroshkevich A.G., Spatial Structure of Perturbations and Origin of Galactic Rotation in Fluctuating Theory, *Astrophysics*, **6**, p.320, 1970.

Our presentation follows the considerations initiated in:

[6] Hamilton A.J.S., Gott J.R., and Weinberg D., The Topology of the Large-Scale Structure of the Universe, *Ap. J.*, **309**, p.1, 1986.

In the cosmological context the minimal-spanning-tree technique was introduced in:

[7] Barrow J.D., Bhavsar S.P., and Sonoda D.H., Minimal Spanning Trees, Filaments and Galaxy Clustering, *Mon. Not. Royal Astr. Soc.*, **216**, p.17, 1985.

The wavelet transform method is described in:

[8] Combes J.M., Grossmann A., and Tchamitchian P. (Eds.), *Wavelets*, Springer-Verlag, 1988.

[9] Slezak E., Bijaoui A., and Mars G., Identification of Structures from Galaxy Counts: Use of the Wavelet Transform, *Astr. Ap.*, **227**, p.301, 1990.

Chapter 7

FILAMENTS AND LIGHT-TRAVEL EFFECTS

> *Man is enabled by abstract*
> *aesthetic contemplation to achieve*
> *conscious unity with the universal.*
> **Piet Mondrian**

Until now we have been studying the internal dynamics of clusters of galaxies treated as systems of pointlike objects interacting via Newtonian gravity. The use of Newtonian dynamics is clearly justified in this problem. However, when considering filaments on scales of the order of the horizon, one can no longer ignore both relativistic and cosmological effects, namely light-cone effects and the Hubble expansion. The accurate treatment of these effects is another important aspect of large-scale cosmology, since it provides the opportunity to obtain values for the key parameters describing the observed Universe. Before taking up this problem let us recall the basics of relativistic cosmology.

7.1   Dynamical Equations of Cosmology

According to General Relativity the World is a $4D$-manifold W endowed with a pseudo-Riemannian (Lorentzian) metric g of signature $(-, +, +, +)$, its associated Levi-Civita connection ∇ and given tensor (or spinor) fields determining the energy-momentum tensor $\mathbf{T}$. Here and below we use the term World to denote the $(3+1)D$ spacetime manifold to distinguish it from its $3D$ spatial cross-section, referred to as the Universe.

These mathematical objects all have a definite physical meaning: the points of the manifold W represent space-time events, the metric and its connection $(\mathbf{g}, \nabla)$ describe gravity (the geometry of the World) and the tensor field $\mathbf{T}$ describes the energy-momentum distribution of the matter fields other than gravity.

The metric and energy-momentum tensor satisfy the Einstein equation

$$\mathbf{G} = 8\pi\mathbf{T} \ , \tag{7.1}$$

where

$$\mathbf{G} = Ric - (1/2)R\mathbf{g} \tag{7.2}$$

is the Einstein tensor and Ric and R are the Ricci tensor and scalar curvature of the metric. The Einstein equation can be considered as a dynamical equation determining the evolution of the Universe as a $3D$-manifold with matter fields evolving in a $(3 + 1)D$-manifold, provided appropriate initial conditions on some spatial cross-section are given (the initial Universe).

Unfortunately, it is not yet known how to find the general solution of the Einstein equation. For this reason people usually start by choosing assumptions which on the one hand, simplify the Einstein equation enough to permit one to find some particular solutions or classes of such solutions, and on the other hand, more or less have observational and theoretical support. The most common and most fruitful assumption is that the Universe is both homogeneous and isotropic in the lowest degree of approximation.

For such a spatially homogeneous and isotropic World one can choose a coordinate system in which the metric can be represented in the Robertson-Walker form:

$$\mathbf{g} = a^2(\eta)(-\mathbf{d}\eta^2 + \mathbf{d}\chi^2 + \Sigma^2(\chi)[\mathbf{d}\theta^2 + \sin^2(\theta)\mathbf{d}\phi^2]), \tag{7.3}$$

in terms of the conformal time η or

$$\mathbf{g} = -\mathbf{d}t^2 + a^2(t)(\mathbf{d}\chi^2 + \Sigma^2(\chi)[\mathbf{d}\theta^2 + \sin^2(\theta)\mathbf{d}\phi^2]) \tag{7.4}$$

in terms of the more usual cosmological proper time t, related to each other by $a(\eta)\mathbf{d}\eta = \mathbf{d}t$, and where

$$\Sigma(\chi) = \begin{cases} \chi & k = 0, \\ \sin(\chi) & k = +1, \\ \sinh(\chi) & k = -1 \end{cases} \tag{7.5}$$

is the function determining the spatial curvature properties of the Universe (Figure 44).

Note that this metric only determines the local properties of a Robertson-Walker World. For example, the flat Universe for which $k = 0$ may have

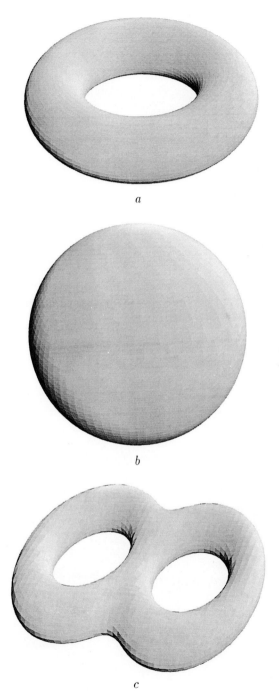

a

b

c

Figure 44 *Different types of homogeneous geometries. (a)* $k = 0$; *(b)* $k = +1$; *(c)* $k = -1$.

many different topologies, among which are those of

$$R^3, \ R^2 \times S^1, \ R^1 \times Tor^2, \ Tor^3 \ ,$$

as partially shown in (Figure 45). The same is true for the other values of k. For example, the Universe can be compact but have negative curvature $k = -1$. Therefore we avoid the often used terms *"closed"* and *"open"* Universe when referring to the value of k, since they do not adequately describe the situation. Instead, for example, by the term *"closed Universe"* we should understand *"compact + without boundary"*.

The constant-time cross-sections of the Robertson-Walker world are maximally symmetric spaces (the Universe at a given time) with the positive-definite 3-metric **h** and its isotropic Riemannian 3-curvature tensor ^3Riem given by

$$\mathbf{h} = a^2(\mathbf{d}\chi^2 + \Sigma^2(\chi)[\mathbf{d}\theta^2 + \sin^2(\theta)\mathbf{d}\phi^2]) \ , \tag{7.6}$$

$$^3Riem_{ijkl} = (k/a^2)[h_{ik}h_{jl} - h_{il}h_{jk}] \ . \tag{7.7}$$

As a result of this symmetry the evolution of such a Universe is determined by the single scale factor function $a(t)$, provided that the matter fields are given. These latter fields must also be spatially homogeneous and isotropic.

It is convenient to describe such matter fields using an ideal fluid model, for which the energy-momentum tensor has the form

$$\mathbf{T} = (\rho + p)\mathbf{u} \otimes \mathbf{u} + p\mathbf{g} \ , \tag{7.8}$$

where ρ, p and $\mathbf{u}$ denote the matter energy density, pressure and 4-velocity respectively. The Einstein equation (7.1) for the World with a Robertson-Walker metric (7.4) and an ideal fluid matter (7.8) present has the following simple form

$$\left(\frac{\dot{a}}{a}\right)^2 + \frac{k}{a^2} \ = \ \frac{8\pi}{3}\rho, \tag{7.9}$$

$$2\frac{\ddot{a}}{a} + \left(\frac{\dot{a}}{a}\right)^2 + \frac{k}{a^2} \ = \ -8\pi p, \tag{7.10}$$

$$(\rho a^3)^{\cdot} \ = \ -p(a^3)^{\cdot} \ , \tag{7.11}$$

where the dot indicates the cosmic time derivative. The last equation is just the energy relation $dE = -pdV$ for the fluid. The World determined by this system of equations is called the Friedmann World.

a

b

c

Figure 45 *2D-manifolds with k = 0.*

To find particular solutions of these equations one must specify the equation of state for the ideal fluid. Two common choices are made for the early and later phases of the evolution

    a. Radiation dominated Universe with

$$p = (1/3)\rho , \tag{7.12}$$

leading to the solutions (Figures 46, 47)

$$a(\eta) = \begin{cases} A^* \sinh \eta, \\ A^* \eta, \\ A^* \sin \eta, \end{cases} \quad t(\eta) = \begin{cases} A^*(\cosh \eta - 1), & k = -1, \\ A^* \eta^2/2, & k = 0, \\ A^*(1 - \cos \eta), & k = +1; \end{cases} \tag{7.13}$$

where $A^* = (4\pi/3)\rho a^4 = $ const.

    b. Matter dominated (dust-filled) Universe with

$$p = 0 , \tag{7.14}$$

leading to the solutions (Figures 48, 49)

$$a(\eta) = \begin{cases} A(\cosh \eta - 1), \\ A\eta^2/2, \\ A(1 - \cos \eta), \end{cases} \quad t(\eta) = \begin{cases} A(\sinh \eta - \eta), & k = -1, \\ A\eta^3/6, & k = 0, \\ A(\eta - \sin \eta), & k = +1; \end{cases} \tag{7.15}$$

where $A = (2\pi/3)\rho a^3 = $ const.

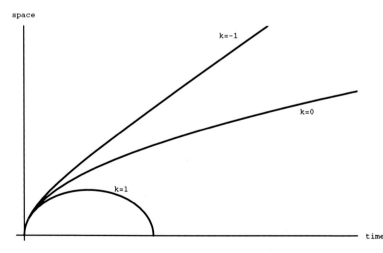

Figure 46 *Solutions of the radiation dominated Universe.*

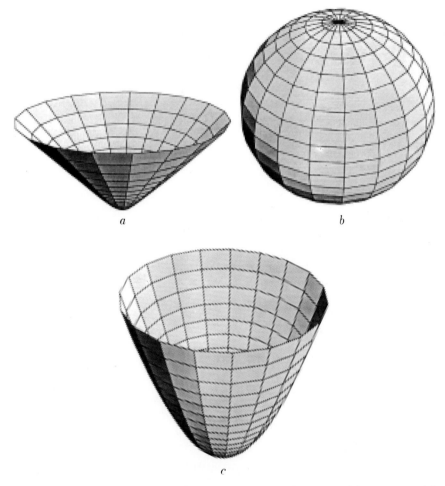

Figure 47 *Radiation dominated 2D Worlds. (a) $k = 0$; (b) $k = +1$; (c) $k = -1$.*

All of these solutions describe an initially expanding Universe, i.e., the scale factor increases as a function of the cosmic time during this phase. There also exist other solutions of the Friedmann equations which correspond to an initially contracting Universe, but if one accepts the observed expansion of the Universe as a fact then only the solutions given above are relevant.

Now let us specify the observable quantities which determine the Friedmann World. To do this consider a light wave emitted at a point with spatial coordinates (χ, θ_e, ϕ_e) at cosmic time $t_e(\eta_e)$ and detected at the point with

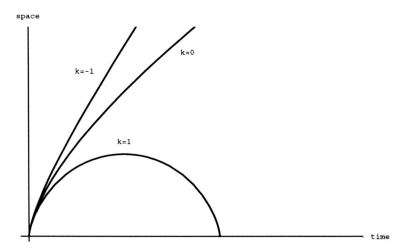

Figure 48 *Solutions of the matter dominated Universe.*

spatial coordinates $(0, \theta_e, \phi_e)$ at time $t_r(\eta_r)$. The difference in the value of the conformal time between these two events is

$$\eta_e - \eta_r = \int_{t_r}^{t_e} \frac{dt}{a(t)} \, .$$

Neglecting the change in the scale factor $a(t)$ during one period δt of the light wave, e.g., that of light in the optical band, one obtains the following relationship between the emitted and detected wavelengths

$$\frac{\lambda_r}{a(t_r)} = \frac{\lambda_e}{a(t_e)} \, ,$$

or

$$\frac{\lambda}{a} = const \, ,$$

and the redshift defined by

$$z = \frac{\lambda_r - \lambda_e}{\lambda_e}$$

has the value

$$z = \frac{a(\eta_r)}{a(\eta_r - \chi)} - 1 \, . \tag{7.16}$$

Making the identification $t_0 = t_r$ of the time of detection with the present time, and letting $t_1 = t_e$ denote the time of emission, one can make the

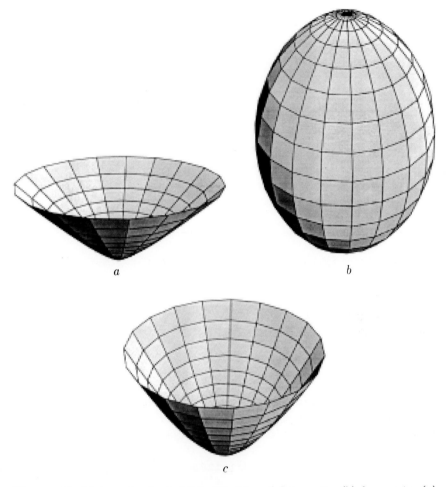

Figure 49 *Matter dominated 2D Worlds.* (a) $k = 0$; (b) $k = +1$; (c) $k = -1$.

expansion

$$z = H_0(t_0 - t_1) + [1 + (q_0/2)]H_0^2(t_0 - t_1)^2 + \cdots ,$$

which is valid if the source of the radiation is not too distant from the receiver. The following notation is used

$$H_0 = \left(\frac{\dot{a}}{a}\right)_0 \, ,$$

$$q_0 = -\left(\frac{a\ddot{a}}{\dot{a}^2}\right)_0 = -\left(\frac{\ddot{a}}{aH^2}\right)_0 \, ,$$

H_0 is the Hubble constant which describes the present rate of expansion, while q_0 is the deceleration constant. The Hubble time H_0^{-1} may be interpreted as the approximate age of the Universe. The remaining observable quantity is the density parameter

$$\Omega = \frac{\rho}{\rho_{cr}} \, , \tag{7.17}$$

where

$$\rho_{cr} = (3H^2/8\pi) \tag{7.18}$$

is the critical density.

These parameters uniquely determine the solutions of the Friedmann equations, and so estimates of their present values obtained from observations can decide which of them describes the state of the Universe in the lowest approximation. For a matter dominated Universe relevant to the later stages of cosmological evolution in which we are interested, the following cases exist

$$\Omega < 1, \, q_0 < \frac{1}{2} \, \leftrightarrow \, k = -1, \text{ infinite expansion,}$$

$$\Omega = 1, \, q_0 = \frac{1}{2} \, \leftrightarrow \, k = 0, \quad \text{infinite expansion (Einstein-de Sitter Universe),}$$

$$\Omega > 1, \, q_0 > \frac{1}{2} \, \leftrightarrow \, k = +1, \text{ expansion to the maximal radius and contraction.}$$

7.2   Light-Cone Effects

Consider the role of light-cone effects on the appearance of matter structures in the Friedmann World. In order to describe the most characteristic features of those effects, let us attribute a homogeneity scale ℓ to the distribution of matter in the Universe. Such a scale, irrespective of its direct meaning as an average separation of superclusters or as a distance characterizing a cellular structure, can again be considered to follow from the assumption that the Universe is spatially homogeneous at large enough length scales (Figure 50).

Let us look for direct observational consequences of that homogeneity scale during the expansion, dealing with the only observable quantity, namely

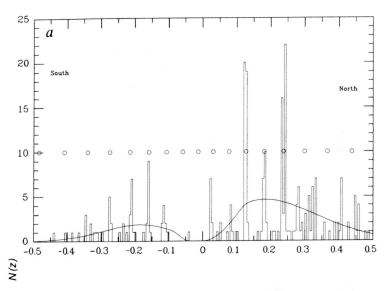

Figure 50 *Distribution of redshifts of galaxies according to pencil-beam surveys; best-fit periods are denoted by circles (from T.L. Broadhurst, R.S. Ellis, D.C. Koo, A. Szalay, Nature, vol.343, p.726, 1990).*

the redshift of an object with a coordinate χ Eq. (7.16)

$$z(\chi) = \frac{a(\eta_p)}{a(\eta_p - \chi)} - 1, \qquad 0 \leq \chi < \eta_p \,, \tag{7.19}$$

where η_p is the value of the conformal time corresponding to the present epoch of observation and the scale factor has the above mentioned values (see Eq. (7.15)).

If the position of the observer is not specifically chosen in space, then one can expect various behaviors in the three different cases of curvature $k = -1, 0, +1$ for the deviation from homogeneity at large redshifts, i.e., in the distribution of objects on the past light cone. As a result one can have modifications of the cellular (lattice) structure depending on the curvature of the Friedmannian Universe.

Consider the role that this effect has in the case of a distribution of matter with peaks located at the following values of χ along some direction (θ, ϕ) at some given epoch of the expansion of the Universe

$$\chi_m = \chi_0 + m\ell, \; m = 0, 1, 2, \dots \,. \tag{7.20}$$

It is convenient to represent the corresponding z-values by a Taylor expansion

$$z_m = z(\chi_0 + m\ell) = \sum_{n=0}^{+\infty} c_n m^n , \qquad (7.21)$$

where

$$0 \le m < \left[\frac{\eta_p - \chi_0}{\ell}\right] ,$$

where the brackets denote the integer part.

The first conclusion which can already be drawn is the inevitable quasiperiodicity of z with some period $z = c_1$ at small m, i.e., for the nearest peaks. Clearly that quasiperiodicity will be violated at larger values of m.

Note also that from the equation

$$z_m = \frac{a(\eta_p)}{a(\eta_p - \chi_0 - m\ell)} - 1 , \qquad (7.22)$$

one could in principle obtain the values of η_p, χ_0, ℓ and k, i.e., the kind of Friedmann Universe would follow from the measured redshifts of the peaks z. However, we propose a more convenient procedure to obtain this cosmological information below.

7.3   Cosmological Parameters

Let us examine the redshifts of the first four peaks, which have the following form in terms of the unknown Taylor coefficients

$$
\begin{aligned}
z_0 &= c_0, \\
z_1 &= c_0 &+c_1 &+c_2 &+c_3 &+O(4), \\
z_2 &= c_0 &+2c_1 &+4c_2 &+8c_3 &+O(4), \\
z_3 &= c_0 &+3c_1 &+9c_2 &+27c_3 &+O(4).
\end{aligned}
$$

This truncated linear system of equations can be inverted to express the coefficients in terms of the z values since its determinant is nonzero

$$\det \begin{pmatrix} 1 & 0 & 0 & 0 \\ 1 & 1 & 1 & 1 \\ 1 & 2 & 4 & 8 \\ 1 & 3 & 9 & 27 \end{pmatrix} = 12 \ne 0 .$$

The result is

$$
\begin{aligned}
c_0 &= & z_0 , \\
c_1 &= (-11/6)z_0 &+3z_1 &-(3/2)z_2 &+(1/3)z_3 , \\
c_2 &= & z_0 &-(5/2)z_1 &+2z_2 &-(1/2)z_3 , \\
c_3 &= (-1/6)z_0 &+(1/2)z_1 &-(1/2)z_2 &+(1/6)z_3 .
\end{aligned}
$$

Since the function $a(\eta)$ in the case of a dust-filled Universe satisfies the first order differential equation

$$a'(\eta) = a(\eta)\sqrt{(A/a(\eta)) - k}$$

containing two parameters A and k, the coefficients of the Taylor expansion of z_m starting from c_3 should depend on the previous three coefficients. In fact one finds

$$c_3 = \frac{c_1}{1 + c_0}\left(\frac{4c_2}{3} - \frac{c_1^2}{2(1 + c_0)}\right) . \tag{7.23}$$

Thus such a dependence between the coefficients implies that the Universe is Friedmann.

In addition to this equation we have three more, and one can readily obtain them from Eqs. (7.21), (7.22)

$$\frac{a(\eta_p)}{a(\eta_p - \chi_0)} = 1 + c_0 , \tag{7.24}$$

$$\frac{A}{a(\eta_p - \chi_0)} = k + \frac{c_1^2}{[(1 + c_0)\ell]^2} , \tag{7.25}$$

$$c_2 - \frac{3c_1^2}{4(1 + c_0)} = (k/4)(1 + c_0)\ell^2 . \tag{7.26}$$

From the last equation one finds

$$k = \text{sign}\left(c_2 - \frac{3c_1^2}{4(1 + c_0)}\right) , \tag{7.27}$$

i.e., the sign of the curvature of the Universe is uniquely determined by coefficients $\{c_n\}$.

To represent the observable cosmological parameters in terms of these coefficients, let us consider the cases $k = 0$ and $k \neq 0$ separately. For $k = 0$ one finds

$$c_2 = \frac{3c_1^2}{4(1 + c_0)} , \tag{7.28}$$

$$\frac{4}{(\eta_p - \chi_0)^2} = \frac{c_1^2}{[(1 + c_0)\ell]^2} , \tag{7.29}$$

$$\frac{\eta_p^2}{\eta_p^2 - \chi_0^2} = 1 + c_0 , \tag{7.30}$$

or

$$\eta_p = \frac{2(1 + c_0)\ell}{c_1(1 - \sqrt{(1 + c_0)/c_0})}. \tag{7.31}$$

$$\chi_0 = \frac{2(1 + c_0)\ell}{c_1(\sqrt{(1 + c_0)/c_0} - 1)}. \tag{7.32}$$

For the case $k \neq 0$, equations (7.24) and (7.25) lead to the result

$$\frac{A}{a(\eta_p - \chi_0)} = \frac{k}{[4c_2(1 + c_0)]/c_1^2 - 3}, \tag{7.33}$$

and

$$\ell^2 = \frac{4k}{1 + c_0}\left(c_2 - \frac{3c_1^2}{4(1 + c_0)}\right), \tag{7.34}$$

so that Eqs. (7.24), (7.33) can be written in the form

$$\frac{b(\eta_p)}{b(\eta_p - \chi_0)} = 1 + c_0, \tag{7.35}$$

$$b(\eta_p - \chi_0) = k\left(\frac{4c_2(1 + c_0)}{c_1^2} - 3\right) = kc, \tag{7.36}$$

where

$$b(\eta) = \begin{cases} 1 - \cos\eta & k = +1, \\ \cosh\eta - 1 & k = -1. \end{cases}$$

Finally from Eqs. (7.35), (7.36) one finds

$$b(\eta_p) = kc(1 + c_0), \tag{7.37}$$

leading to estimates for the present value of the conformal time and the size of the Universe.

Thus by obtaining the four coefficients c_n from observations, namely by means of the estimates for the redshifts of the peaks of the matter distribution in different directions obtained from pencil-beam surveys, one can use the formulas derived above to obtain rather valuable information on the cosmological parameters. In particular, if $k = 0$, then the present value of the conformal time η_p is uniquely determined by the homogeneity scale, while if $k = +1$ or $k = -1$, the scale ℓ is uniquely determined by all four coefficients.

In conclusion we emphasize that this entire analysis requires only the assumption of the homogeneity and isotropy of the Universe.

Bibliography

There are a number of nice books on General Relativity and Cosmology. We mention the following classic ones:

[1] Misner C.W., Thorne K.S., and Wheeler J.A., *Gravitation*, Freeman, San Francisco, 1973.

[2] Hawking S.W. and Ellis G.F.R., *The Large Scale Structure of Space-Time*, Cambridge University Press, 1973.

Evidence for apparent regularity in the galaxy distribution with some characteristic scale (128 Mpc) has been obtained from deep pencil-beam surveys:

[3] Broadhurst T.L., Ellis R.S., Koo D.C. and Szalay A.S. Large-Scale Distribution of Galaxies at the Galactic Poles, *Nature*, **343**, p.726, 1990.

Chapter 8

THE COSMIC BACKGROUND RADIATION AS A TRACER OF GEOMETRY OF THE UNIVERSE

Light is similar to water;
in each case it makes its way through.
Jean-Dominique Ingres.

8.1 The Crucial Feature of the Background Radiation

The Cosmic Microwave Background (Relic) Radiation (CMB) is one of the fundamental observational facts which most determines our present knowledge of the early evolution of the Universe. The features of the CMB undoubtedly carry the fingerprints of various physical phenomena which occurred in the early stages of the Universe. In the Big Bang theory it carries unique information about the state of the Universe both before and after the epoch of recombination at $z \simeq 1000$. However, here we will not attempt to discuss all the aspects of the role of the CMB within Big Bang cosmology, as it is a topic for a comprehensive volume. Moreover we will not even discuss all the phenomena related to one of its properties—the anisotropy; those phenomena include the Silk effect, the Sachs-Wolfe effect, the Rees-Sciama effect, the Sunyaev-Zeldovich effect, gravitational lensing, and other effects which are described in the literature. Instead, we shall concentrate on the anisotropy properties of the CMB as a source of direct information about the large-scale structure of the Universe from the same geometrical perspective as we did in the case of the matter distribution.

The choice of the problem of the anisotropy of the CMB is not arbitrary since just this observational fact alone may serve as the milestone for the basics of Big Bang cosmology.

In our considerations we are faced with the problem of investigating how the properties of a beam of geodesics depend on the geometrical and topological properties of the Universe. As indicated earlier the correlation function is a rather informative tool in determining the behavior of a geodesic flow. In particular this function decays exponentially if the flow is an Anosov system. This fact is of special importance to us. It is remarkable that the KS-entropy characterizing the time scale of that decay depends only on the size of the Friedmann Universe.

It appears that observable statistical effects like the smoothness of the CMB as determined by the evolution of small perturbations and hence by the properties of the space-time manifold, in certain cases can be indicators of the latter, thus completing the information derived from the matter distribution.

Essential cosmological constraints can be derived of course from the anisotropy features of the CMB if combined with the data on the large-scale structure in the framework of gravitational instability theory, though it requires certain additional assumptions at least regarding the spectrum of initial fluctuations, the Harrison-Zeldovich spectrum being the most conventional, biased dark matter models.

8.2   Free Motion in the World

We now address the question of how one describes the free motion of photons in the World. To make matters simpler we will only consider a Friedmann World W, decomposed into a homogeneous $3D$ Universe characterized by some coordinates x, evolving with respect to the cosmic time t. Thus each event in the World can be assigned unique space-time coordinates (x, t).

One can then project any trajectory $\gamma(\cdot)$ from the World W into the Universe U simply by associating to $\gamma(\lambda) = (x(\lambda), \lambda)$ the curve $c(\lambda) = x(\lambda)$. It turns out that null geodesics in the World project onto geodesics in the Universe with a new affine parameter.

Let W be a $4D$ manifold with a Lorentzian metric $^4\mathbf{g}$ which is oriented and time-oriented. Let M be a $3D$ manifold and let

$$\imath : M \to W \;,$$

be an embedding of M in W such that the embedded manifold $\imath(M) = U$ is spacelike, i.e., the induced metric $\imath^*(^4\mathbf{g}) = \mathbf{g}$ is a Riemannian metric on M. Let $C^\infty_{space}(M;W,{}^4\mathbf{g})$ denote the set of all such spacelike embeddings for which the embedded manifold is smooth.

Now consider a curve in $C^\infty_{space}(M;W,{}^4\mathbf{g})$, i.e., a curve $\imath_t$ of spacelike embeddings of M into $(W,{}^4\mathbf{g})$. The tangent vector to this curve

$$\frac{d\imath_t}{dt} \equiv \mathbf{Y}_{\imath_t} = \mathbf{Y}_{U_t} \circ \imath_t : M \to TW$$

defines a one-parameter family of vector fields $\mathbf{Y}_{U_t}$ on the embedded hypersurfaces $U_t \equiv \imath_t(M)$. The normal and tangential projections of Y_{U_t} define a curve of functions

$$N_t = \mathbf{Y}_\perp : M \to R$$

and vector fields

$$\mathbf{X}_t = \mathbf{Y}_\parallel : M \to TM$$

on M through the equation

$$\mathbf{Y}_{U_t} \circ \imath_t(x) = \mathbf{Y}_\perp(x,t)\mathbf{Z}_{U_t} \circ \imath_t(x) + (\imath_t)_*|_x \mathbf{Y}_\parallel(x,t) \;,$$

where $\mathbf{Z}_{U_t}$ is the forward-pointing unit timelike normal to U_t.

Assume that the map

$$\jmath : M \times R \to W : (x,t) \mapsto \imath_t(x)$$

is a diffeomorphism. Using $\jmath$ as a coordinate system for W, the metric $^4\mathbf{g}$ of W can be written in the form

$$\jmath^{*4}\mathbf{g} = (\jmath^{*4}\mathbf{g})_{\alpha\beta}\mathbf{dx}^\alpha \otimes \mathbf{dx}^\beta = -N^2\mathbf{dt} \otimes \mathbf{dt} + g_{ab}(\mathbf{dx}^a + X^a\mathbf{dt}) \otimes (\mathbf{dx}^b + X^b\mathbf{dt}) \;.$$

where $g_{ab} = (g_t)_{ab}$ and $\mathbf{g}_t = \imath_t^{*4}\mathbf{g}$ is the spatial metric on M.

Using the map $\jmath$ one can define uniquely the projection π

$$W \xrightarrow{\jmath^{-1}} M \times R$$
$$\searrow \quad \downarrow \pi_M \qquad \pi = \pi_M \circ \jmath^{-1},$$
$$\pi \quad M$$

where

$$\pi_M : M \times R \to M : (x,t) \mapsto x \;,$$

which depends on N and $\mathbf{X}$. This map identifies each spacelike hypersurface of constant time t in the World with the single quotient space M representing the manifold of the Universe without regard to a specific time. It is this correspondence between events in the Universe at different times which identifies a "fixed point of space". It may be used to convert any evolving spatial fields in the Universe to time-dependent fields on the single manifold M of "space".

Given this framework, any curve γ in W can be projected onto a curve c on M as represented by the following diagram

$$
\begin{array}{ccc}
W & \xrightarrow{\pi} & M \\
 & \searrow & \\
\gamma \uparrow & \phi & \uparrow c \\
R & \xrightarrow{\sigma} & R
\end{array}
\qquad
\begin{array}{l}
\sigma = \phi \circ \gamma : R \to R \text{ is a diffeomorphism} \\
c = \pi \circ \gamma \circ \sigma^{-1} : R \to M : \lambda \mapsto c(\lambda).
\end{array}
$$

In this way a worldline in the World is mapped onto a "point moving in space" as the time elapses.

In particular, the worldline of a photon, a null geodesic, projects onto a curve on M which is natural to call its trajectory in space. One can then ask under what conditions is this trajectory in space also a geodesic of the spatial geometry. In other words, what conditions should $({}^4\mathbf{g}, N, \mathbf{X}, \phi)$ satisfy in order that the projection of any null geodesic on W be a geodesic on M with respect to the spatial metric $\mathbf{g}_t$. The following can be shown to be sufficient conditions for this

$$N = 1 \, , \tag{8.1}$$

$$\mathbf{X} = 0 \, , \tag{8.2}$$

$$\mathbf{g} = a^2(t) \cdot \mathbf{h} \, , \tag{8.3}$$

$$\phi(x,t) = \phi_0 + \int_{t_0}^{t} a^{-1}(s)ds \, , \tag{8.4}$$

$$\lambda(t) = \int_{t_0}^{t} a^{-1}(s)ds = \eta(t) - \eta(t_0) \, , \tag{8.5}$$

where $\mathbf{h}$ Eq. (7.6) is the metric of a maximally symmetric $3D$ Riemannian manifold. The time-dependent scale factor $a(t)$ only enters into the relationships between the various parameterizations of the null geodesics and their spatial projections and the cosmic time.

8.3   Photon Beam Mixing in the Closed Friedmann Universe

Next consider the behavior of a beam of null geodesics in a closed homogeneous Universe expressed by using the above spatial projection scheme as a set of spatial trajectories. First recall some of the criteria for classifying dynamical systems based on the properties of correlation functions as discussed in Chapter 2.

There it was remarked that a geodesic flow f on a closed $3D$ Riemannian manifold with negative curvature in all two-dimensional directions is an Anosov system, for which the correlation function (2.23) decreases following an exponential law, i.e., $\exists C_{g_1,g_2} > 0$ such that

$$|b_{g_1,g_2}(t)| \leq C_{g_1,g_2} \cdot \exp(-\beta_{g_1,g_2} h(f) \cdot t) , \qquad (8.6)$$

where $h(f)$ is the KS-entropy of the flow f and

$$t_c = (\beta h(f))^{-1} , \qquad (8.7)$$

is the characteristic decay time for perturbations. Thus by the time $t \gg t_c$ such a flow has completely lost any information about initial conditions.

The property of the decay of the correlation functions can be applied to the problem of the evolution of the perturbations of a photon gas in the closed (compact, without boundary) Friedmann Universe with negative curvature $k = -1$. As noted above in Chapter 7, the homogeneous and isotropic spatial metric does not uniquely specify the global topology of the Universe, which may be chosen to be compact in this case.

Let $W = U \times R$ be a $(3+1)D$ Friedmann World. A null geodesic flow on this World can be reduced to a geodesic flow on the $3D$ closed spatial manifold $M = U$ with metric $\mathbf{h}$ of Eq. (7.6) and affine parameter λ of Eq. (8.5). According to the geodesic deviation theory, the separation of two nearby geodesics in the spatial manifold (with a fixed value of the scale factor) satisfies the relation

$$l(\lambda) = l(0) \exp(\chi \lambda) , \qquad (8.8)$$

where the Lyapunov exponent has the value $\chi = 1$ (compared to $\chi = 0$ when $k = 0$ or $k = +1$) and λ is the affine parameter along the geodesics. The correlation function for a $3D$ geodesic flow decreases like

$$|b(\lambda)| \leq C \exp(-h\lambda) , \qquad (8.9)$$

where using the Pesin formula (5.14) one can readily see that the KS-entropy has the value $h = 2\chi = 2$.

These properties hold for the "frozen" spatial geometry with a fixed value of the scale factor. Re-expressing this description in terms of the true spatial separation as a function of the cosmic time leads to the relation

$$L(t) = L(t_0) \frac{a(t)}{a(t_0)} \exp(\lambda(t)) . \qquad (8.10)$$

For the case of a $k = -1$ Friedmann World using Eq. (7.15) one obtains the following expression for the function $\lambda(t)$ Eq. (8.5)

$$\lambda(t) = \ln\left((1 + z)\left[\frac{1 + \sqrt{1 - \Omega}}{\sqrt{1 + z\Omega} + \sqrt{1 - \Omega}}\right]^2\right) .$$

Any small perturbation of the photon beam, say at the recombination time $z = 1000$, should be smoothed by a factor of (Figure 51)

$$e^{h\lambda} = (1 + z)^2 \left[\frac{1 + \sqrt{1 - \Omega}}{\sqrt{1 + z\Omega} + \sqrt{1 - \Omega}}\right]^4 . \tag{8.11}$$

by the present time at $z = 0$.

For example, for the decrease of perturbations of temperature $\delta T/T$ by now if $\Omega \sim 0.1$ one has

$$(\delta T/T)_{z=0} \simeq (\delta T/T)_{z=1000} \cdot 10^{-3} . \tag{8.12}$$

Thus remarkable smooting of the degree of anisotropy of the CMB existing at the epoch of last scattering can occur by the present time just due to geometrical properties of the Friedmann World.

A similar analysis can be performed for any scale factor function for the Universe with $k = -1$ and $\Omega < 1$. In particular, in the case of an inflationary Universe one has $\Omega = 1$ and $h = 0$ and therefore this effect is absent.

8.4   Degree of Complexity of Anisotropy Spots

These results regarding the behavior of a geodesic flow on a space of negative curvature are a consequence of the Jacobi equation for geodesic deviation on a 3-space of constant curvature k, namely Eqs. (2.7), (7.7)

$$\frac{d^2 \mathbf{n}}{d\lambda^2} + \frac{k}{a^2}\mathbf{n} = 0 , \tag{8.13}$$

where $\mathbf{n}$ is the deviation vector determining the behavior of nearby geodesics. This equation has the following solutions for the three cases of interest

$$\mathbf{n}(\lambda) = \begin{cases} \mathbf{n}(0) + \dot{\mathbf{n}}(0)\lambda & k = 0 , \\ \mathbf{n}(0)\cos(\lambda/a) + \dot{\mathbf{n}}(0)\sin(\lambda/a) & k = +1 , \\ \mathbf{n}(0)\cosh(\lambda/a) + \dot{\mathbf{n}}(0)\sinh(\lambda/a) & k = -1 . \end{cases} \tag{8.14}$$

These three types of solutions have very different properties. To appreciate these differences, consider the evolution of a gas of particles with velocity vectors isotropically (randomly) distributed within a ball in position space

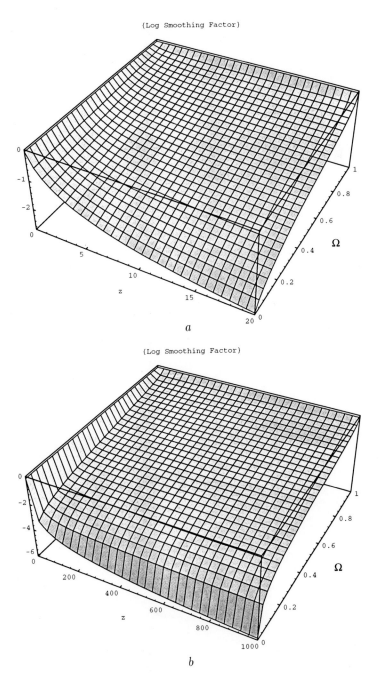

Figure 51 *Smoothing factor $e^{h\lambda}$; (a) $0 \leq z \leq 20$; (b) $0 \leq z \leq 1000$.*

with unit radius. Moreover, partition this unit ball in the position space into smaller subsets, each with particles with nearly the same velocity. According to Eq. (8.14) the behavior of the small subsets is quite different depending on the sign of k. This results in very different behaviors for the original unit ball as it evolves, as illustrated in Figure 52.

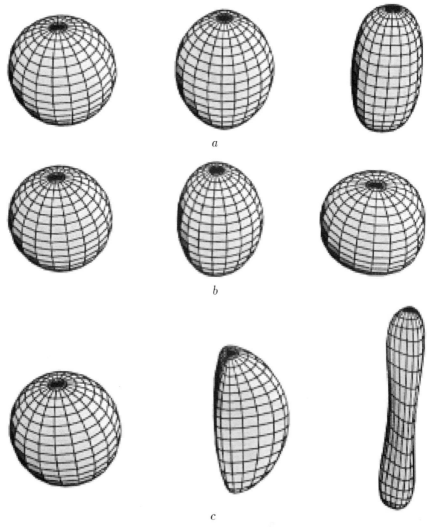

Figure 52 *The evolution of a unit ball in the Universe with different curvatures: (a) $k = 0$; (b) $k = +1$; (c) $k = -1$.*

In particular, in the $k = -1$ case the geodesic flow is an Anosov system (locally, if U is not compact). Therefore, if the initial distribution of velocity of particles within the ball is random, the evolution of a perturbed ball in U should appear as a multitail complex structure which is the union of elongated ellipsoids, while for $k = 0$ and $k = +1$ it should appear as a union of the slightly changed balls. This effect arises for the following reason. The initial ball has a regular form (ball) in position space but a rather complicated form (multitail structure) in velocity space. During the evolution for $k = -1$ where one has an Anosov system with an exponential mixing (homogeneous mixing), the form of the evolving set in position space, due to small inhomogeneity of the Universe, will become similar to that of the one in velocity space (elongated, multitail structure). At the epoch up to the decoupling one, the contribution to the mixing effect can be due to relativistic matter.

As a result one may have different geometrical features of the CMB sky maps, namely the shapes of structures formed by curves of constant temperature—the anisotropy spots, for various values of k. Multitail, elongated spots occur for $k = -1$, while for $k = 0$ and $k = +1$ no such effect exists due to the absence of an exponential instability (mixing). In these cases the spots could resemble circles, say, at 3σ-level cuts, i.e., after the extraction of the contribution of Gaussian random field fluctuations. Let us again emphasize that in a strongly homogeneous Universe null geodesics cannot lead to any image-distortion on the light cone; similarly it does not make much sense to talk about the smoothing of the CMB temperature if there were no initial fluctuations.

Recall also that the final structure resulting from such an evolution from the recombination time to the present should increase in size by a factor of

$$1 + z \simeq 1000$$

due to the expansion of the Universe. The present amplitude and the degree of elongation of perturbations in the CMB depend on the curvature of the present Universe and its age.

This effect occurs only in the Universe with negative curvature $k = -1$ and is absent when either $k = 1$ or $k = 0$. The last case occurs in the inflationary scenario, i.e., when the Universe is flat or is so large that can be considered as flat as well. Thus a unique parameter appears, **the degree of elongation**—a simpler indicator of the **degree of complexity**, which can be rather informative concerning the main parameters of the Universe. The elongated figures evidently should have a *random* angular distribution. In principle both these features may distinguish this effect from the contribution of the Sachs-Wolfe effect and some other well-known effects; for

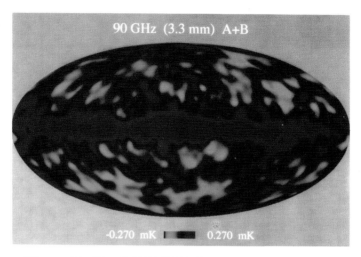

Figure 53 *The COBE-DMR first year map at 90 GHz.*

example, distortion of images due to cosmic strings presumably should have an oriented character.

Recalling, for example, the COBE-DMR first-year full-sky maps (Figure 53) one has the impression that their structure more closely resembles the pattern for $k = -1$ than the other cases. However, due to the dominance of noise in these maps the final conclusion requires either more sophisticated analysis or more accurate data.

The dependence of the anisotropy structures on the wavelength of measurements could indicate that the isotropy level was different for various energies at the decoupling epoch.

Thus if this image-distortion effect can be seen in the CMB sky maps, then one can draw important conclusions about the sign of the curvature of the Universe and the value of the density parameter Ω. Constraints on the values of other cosmological parameters could be evaluated from the degree of elongation as well.

8.5   Photons, Billiards, Ink Drops, Etc.

What is the key aspect of the CMB isotropy problem which requires the use of ergodic theory? The key point is that it is necessary to examine the propagation of a photon beam and not that of a single photon. More precisely, the problem must be reduced to the study of a geodesic flow using correlation functions, not just the equation of a single geodesic.

To illustrate the crucial role of this approach let us recall the problem of an ideal gas; the latter as is well known was introduced in the last century as a good model for explaining various physical phenomena. However, it was realized quite soon that a system of particles interacting only by elastic scattering must somehow follow the process of reaching equilibrium familiar from common experience, i.e., must evolve so that it smoothly covers the energy hypersurface without any exchange of energy between the particles.

The hope of explaining this problem was initially associated with the so-called ergodic conjecture concerning the property permitting the system phase point to pass as close as desired to any point of the phase space after a long enough time. The first person who realized that ergodicity alone is not sufficient to enable the system to reach an equilibrium state was J.W. Gibbs, the founder of statistical mechanics. He introduced the concept of systems possessing the property of mixing.

The rigorous study of systems with these properties is the subject of ergodic theory, as introduced in Chapter 2. In particular, it has been shown that the correlation functions do not decay for purely ergodic systems, while they do for mixing ones. The rate of that decay can be both polynomial and exponential; in the latter case one also has a natural time scale for this decay.

The achievements of ergodic theory also concern the ideal gas problem, especially in the study of various billiard-type systems, the Sinai billiard being the best known of these. The characteristic parameters of these systems, the mixing of their trajectories, and hence the smoothing of initial perturbations can be studied, though usually it is not a simple task. However, if one follows the trajectory of a single particle, i.e., a single molecule of the gas, one will not notice any change in energy. *The effect of smoothing is a purely statistical one.*

A similar case concerns the photon gas in a compact Universe, where according to Big Bang theory, after the last scattering photons propagate freely, i.e., without a change in energy. To be precise one should note, that for example, due to the Sunyaev-Zeldovich effect, i.e., due to inverse Compton scattering on hot electrons in optically thin clusters of galaxies, relic photons can change their energy.

The problem of the behaviour of perturbations of photon gas in the Universe thus amounts to the study of the mixing properties of the flow of geodesics; the study of billiards has shown that these properties are determined by the curvature of the scattering surfaces and the metric of the space of motion. As indicated above, the beam of geodesics in a Friedmann World with a compact Universe of negative curvature has properties similar to mixing billiards with correlation functions decaying by an exponential law, the smoothing factor depending on the size of the Universe via the KS-entropy.

It is worth mentioning that although the above analysis was carried out for spatially homogeneous and isotropic worlds, the results also remain valid for the more realistic case, namely for the perturbed spaces with these backgrounds. The reason is as follows. Since the null geodesics in a Friedmann $4D$-manifold are also geodesics on the quotient space with a fixed scale factor, the parameter λ depends on the position x. The perturbed system then is equivalent to geodesic flow on a $3D$-space with perturbed but nearly constant curvature. Because of the structural stability (coarseness) of Anosov systems, the perturbed systems are also Anosov systems.

Due to essential differences between the null and space-like $4D$ geodesic flows present in the two integrals

$$\lambda(t) = \begin{cases} c \int^t a^{-1}(s)ds & \text{null case ,} \\ c_1 \int^t \dfrac{ds}{a(s)[c_2^2 + a^2(s)]^{1/2}} & \text{time-like case ,} \end{cases}$$

where c, c_1, c_2 are constants, the characteristic time scale for photons is much smaller than for particles with non-zero mass. Therefore, photons have time to mix, while matter does not.

We note another remarkable consequence of this mixing phenomena. The agreement of the temperature of the CMB at opposite sides of the sky to a sufficiently high level is usually considered to require an inevitable causal connection of those regions. To explain this phenomenon, known as the horizon problem, is one of the goals of many theories and scenarios, including inflation.

However, due to the mixing effect of a geodesic flow, one can have in principle two close temperatures in directions which are not causally related since the decay of small perturbations, the mixing of trajectories and hence the smoothing of initial temperature anisotropy are determined only by the properties of the space-time manifold: *two ink drops in a same cup of water mix in the same manner without requiring information about each other.*

In some sense one can also compare this situation with numerous other facts, e.g., why two atoms in different regions of the Universe are emitting photons of exactly of the same energy having no exchange of information.

Indeed, although a single given geodesic is not complicated and does not possess any random features, if one tries to look the cuts of any fixed subset of phase space of a hyperbolic system at given periods of time, the properties of complexity and randomness will appear readily. The problem in this formulation can be attributed to the study of *random sequences* introduced by Kolmogorov and Chaitin in 1960's.

From the point of view of the observer the loss of information is determined by the impossibility even in principle of reconstructing the initial trajectories of the photons during the measurements within certain angle and period of time, so that the averaged value on temperature anisotropy $\delta T/T$ should be suppressed as compared with the surface of last scattering.

The *horizon problem* should therefore be attributed only to those observational facts which really require exchange of information.

Thus the isotropy properties of the CMB can yield immediate information about the global parameters of the Universe, in particular determining its curvature k and Ω.

Although certain observational arguments, including those based on the large scale distribution of matter and the motion of galaxies, support the estimate $\Omega < 1$, the situation is far from clear. It cannot be excluded that through anisotropy measurements of the CMB the effect of relic photon mixing might be useful in deriving direct information about Ω, existence of dark matter and other cosmological parameters.

The effect of the isotropization of the CMB once again demonstrates the deep underlying relationship between the concepts of loss of information, randomness, entropy and temperature on one hand, and their description by instability properties of dynamical systems, on the other hand. For the first case one has the classic example of Hawking radiation. Concerning the second we mention the remark by Prigogine (private communication, 1993) that the Big Bang itself can be considered as an instability of some properly defined dynamical system.

Bibliography

For a review of the status of the CMB see:

[1] Silk J., The Cosmic Microwave Background, *Physica Scripta*, **T36**, p.16, 1991 (Talk at Nobel Symposium no.79).

[2] Peebles P.J.E. *Principles of Physical Cosmology*, Princeton University Press, 1993.

The study of properties of geodesics on manifolds with negative curvature goes back to:

[3] Hadamard G., Les Surfaces a Courbures Opposees et Leur Ligues Geodesiques, *Journ. Mat. Pur. Appl.*, **4**, p.27, 1898;

and was continued in:

[4] Hedlund G., The Dynamics of Geodesic Flows, *Bull. Amer. Math. Soc.*, **45**, p.241, 1939;

[5] Hopf E., Statistik der Geodätischen Linien in Mannigfaltigkeiten Negativer Krümmung, *Ber. Verhandl. Sächs. Akad. Wiss. Leipsiz*, **91**, p.261, 1939;

[6] Anosov D.V., Geodesic Flows on Closed Riemannian Manifolds with Negative Curvature, *Proceed. Steklov Institute of Mathematics*, **90**, 1967.

The study of *random sequences* was initiated in:

[7] Kolmogorov A.N., Three Approaches to the Quantitative Definition of Information, *Problems of Information Transmission*, **1**, no.1, p.3, 1965.

[8] Kolmogorov A.N., On the Logical Foundations of the Information Theory and Probability Theory, *Problems of Information Transmission*, .5, no.3, p.3, 1969.

For Chaitin's results we refer to:

[9] Chaitin G.J., *Information-Theoretic Incompleteness*, World Scientific, Singapore, 1992.

The projection of geodesics from the 4-manifold to the spatial 3-manifold has been considered in:

[10] Lockhart C.M., Misra B., and Prigogine I., Geodesic Instability and Internal Time in Relativistic Cosmology, *Phys. Rev.*, **D25**, p.921, 1982.

The rate of mixing for geodesic flows on hyperbolic manifolds can be found in:

[11] Pollicott M., Exponential Mixing for the Geodesic Flow on Hyperbolic Three-Manifolds, *Journ. Stat. Phys.*, **67**, p.667, 1992.

Estimates for anisotropy limits on the CMB are derived in:

[12] Gurzadyan V.G., Kocharyan A.A., On the Problem of Isotropization of Cosmic Microwave Background Radiation, *Astr. Ap.*, **260**, p.14, 1992.

The importance of the study of the geometrical shapes of the anisotropies on CMB sky maps is stressed in:

[13] Gurzadyan V.G., Kocharyan A.A., Anisotropy of Cosmic Microwave Background Radiation: A Test for Inflation and Ω, *Europhys. Lett.*, **22**, p.231, 1993.

[14] Gurzadyan V.G., Kocharyan A.A., A New View on the Problem of Anisotropy of the Cosmic Background Radiation, *Int. Journ. Mod. Phys.*, **2D**, p.97, 1993.

Estimates for Ω based on the motions of galaxies and large-scale data are discussed for example in:

[15] Huchra J., Large Scale Structure and Inflation, in: *Observational Tests of Inflation*, Ed. T. Shanks et al. (NATO Workshop), Kluwer, 1991.

[16] Salucci P., Persic M., Borgani S., A Measurement of Ω_0 from the Internal Dynamics of Spiral Galaxies, *Ap. J.*, **405**, p.459, 1993.

EPILOGUE

I believe in everlastingness.
I never finish a painting—
I just stop working on it for a while.
Arshile Gorky Adoian

We have come to the end of our story.

We have mentioned some observational data which undoubtedly will be revised in the near future and thereafter. We have described some methods which hopefully should lead to other new and more sophisticated ones. We have made some predictions which do not necessarily have to be confirmed exactly.

It might seem amazing but in our theoretical survey we have deliberately avoided the discussion of any one of numerous models or scenarios describing the origin of observed structures, even the popular ones, or of their apparent success and gaps.

We have only dealt with the paradigms of the large-scale Universe which can be asserted within present scientific doctrines, keeping in mind that the content of the latter is also subject to change with time.

In essence, this survey has undertaken a step towards the understanding of the observed Universe as a union of Chaos and Order. Already the problem of the Cosmic Background Radiation demonstrates that limitations imposed in principle by complete randomness and unpredictability in the spirit of the Gödel-Chaitin incompleteness theorems are coming to add ever mysterious shade to that union. These concepts themselves perhaps can be attributed to the emerging scientific doctrines of our time.

Realizing our typical place (although every epoch offers a hope to argue to the contrary) in this ever-changing, interdependent and multi-leveled experience, we can clearly feel the relative nature of our local absolutes.

This epilogue is therefore a prologue for a new and much more breathtaking scene.

The curtain is rising ...

Index